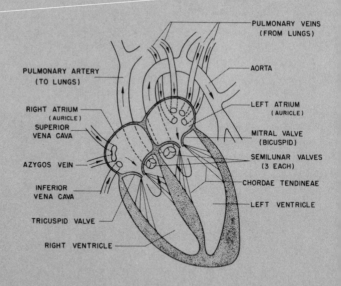

PULMONARY VEINS
(FROM LUNGS)

AORTA

PULMONARY ARTERY
(TO LUNGS)

LEFT ATRIUM
(AURICLE)

RIGHT ATRIUM
(AURICLE)

SUPERIOR
VENA CAVA

MITRAL VALVE
(BICUSPID)

AZYGOS VEIN

SEMILUNAR VALVES
(3 EACH)

CHORDAE TENDINEAE

INFERIOR
VENA CAVA

LEFT VENTRICLE

TRICUSPID VALVE

RIGHT VENTRICLE

CIRCULATION

and

RESPIRATION

The Evolution of an Idea

MARK GRAUBARD
University of Minnesota

Harcourt, Brace & World, Inc.
New York and Burlingame

B.4.65

© 1964 by Harcourt, Brace & World, Inc.

Library of Congress Catalog Card Number: 64–18773

Printed in the United States of America

Preface

The purpose of this volume is to trace the full course of development of our scientific conception of the flow of blood in the vertebrate organism and the incipient notion of its role. This task is carried out by the reproduction of significant excerpts from the works of seventeen key contributors, from Aristotle to Borelli, with each text followed by a commentary to highlight the aim, approach, difficulties, and achievements of the scientist. The actual thoughts and experiments of the selected men of genius provide a historical background revealing to the reader, perhaps for the first time, the real and unadorned struggle of the human mind to uncover and explain a relatively simple and attainable facet of nature, in this case within the realm of biology. This treatment exposes many past misconceptions concerning the method of science in general and the growth of the idea of the circulation in particular.

The text is not just a factual history of the discovery of the nature of circulation and respiration. It shows how an intelligent individual may, through observation and a careful analysis of his findings with exercise of the imagination, reach brilliant and farsighted conclusions. It cites reasons for the prevalence of theories that have had to be discarded, pointing out the obstacles on the way to acceptance of today's recognized theory. It stresses the role of the model in science and indicates the mode of replacement of an established model by a better, more functional, and more productive one. The commentaries continually emphasize the value of well-disciplined scientific thought.

Although the papers assembled deal only with the discovery of the blood's flow, and refer sketchily to the problem of the blood's oxygenation and transport, the study reveals nonetheless the never-ending expansion of scientific inquiry and the manner in which scientific knowledge and understanding grow.

March, 1964   MARK GRAUBARD

Contents

PREFACE   v

1. *The Nature of Scientific Progress*   *1*

2. ARISTOTLE
The History of Animals [HISTORIA ANIMALIUM]   *5*
The First Account   *10*

3. GALEN
On Anatomical Procedures [DE ANATOMICIS
     ADMINISTRATIONIBUS]   *13*
On the Functions of Parts of the Human Body [DE USU
     PARTIUM CORPORIS HUMANI]   *25*
On the Natural Faculties [PERI PHYSIKON DYNAMEON]   *36*
Galen on the Functions of Blood   *41*

4. IBN NAFIS
A Thirteenth-Century Manuscript on Blood   *59*
The Galenic Foundation   *63*

5. ANDREAS VESALIUS
The Epitome   *67*
Vesalius Accepts and Passes On   *73*

6. MICHAEL SERVETUS
The Restoration of Christianity [CHRISTIANISMI
     RESTITUTIO]   *83*
Servetus and His Accidental Discovery   *90*

7. REALDUS COLUMBUS
Of Things Anatomical [DE RE ANATOMICA]   *93*
The Meticulous Anatomist   *100*

8. ANDREAS CAESALPINUS

PERIPATETIC QUESTIONS [QUAESTIONUM
  PERIPATETICARUM]   103
Caesalpinus Meanders, Hits, and Misses   115

9. HIERONYMUS FABRICIUS

Valves of Veins [DE VENARUM OSTIOLIS]   119
*A Valuable Contribution, Small and Wrongly
  Understood*   126

10. WILLIAM HARVEY

On the Motion of the Heart and Blood in Animals   129
Harvey's Discovery by Insight and Synthesis   170

11. MARCELLO MALPIGHI

Epistle I (to Giovanni Borelli)   177
Epistle II (to Giovanni Borelli)   180
Malpighi Discerns the Proof of the Circulation   184

12. ANTONY VAN LEEUWENHOEK

On the Circulation of the Blood   187
Leeuwenhoek's "Trifling Observations"   193

13. PHILOSOPHICAL
    TRANSACTIONS

*An Account of more Tryals of Transfusion, accompanied
  with some Considerations thereon*   197
Early Transfusions and a Warning   204

14. ROBERT HOOKE

An Account of an Experiment made by Mr. Hook   207
A Model Experiment by Hooke   210

15. RICHARD LOWER

Treatise on the Heart [TRACTATUS DE CORDE]   213
The Modern Approach of Lower   226

16. JOHN MAYOW

Medico-Physical Works [TRACTATUS QUINQUE MEDICO-
        PHYSICI]   229
Mayow Explores the Mechanism of Respiration   239

17. ROBERT BOYLE

Suspicions About Some Hidden Qualities in the Air   241
*Some Additional Experiments Relating to the Suspicions
        About the Hidden Qualities of the Air*   248
Physico-mechanical Experiments   250
New Vistas Are Opened by Boyle   257

18. GIOVANNI ALFONSO BORELLI

On the Movements of Animals [DE MOTU ANIMALIUM]   259
The Heart as Muscle Tissue, According to Borelli   263

19. *The Intricacy of Scientific Advance*   267

INDEX   274

1.
The Nature of Scientific Progress

We are accustomed to view the road of
scientific development as one that, once
begun, climbs steadily upward, expanding
in width and multiplying its ramifications
in various directions. Under normal conditions such progress may indeed be observed, but unfortunately normal conditions do not always hold. Thus, history
may present us with a situation in which
contingent circumstances may inhibit altogether even the germination of a science.
This happened in ancient Palestine, where
the Hebrew culture focused all enthusiasm upon its newly found faith in one
spiritual God and was obliged to battle
the seductiveness of the Babylonian religion, which centered around the worship
of celestial bodies, the planets. Hebrew
law chose to prohibit not only planetary
worship but even the study of celestial motions. Similarly, in its fight against the idol
worship of paganism, it proscribed all
painting and sculpture.

Greek culture, on the other hand, laid
solid foundations in a variety of scientific
disciplines, such as zoology, botany, physiology, geometry, astronomy, arithmetic,
and medicine, and made significant advances as well in philosophy, art, literature, and metaphysics. Nevertheless, in

time, many of the sciences came to a standstill, and with the coming of Christianity, all interest in science seemed to cease entirely for several centuries. The lively minds of the period were fascinated by the concepts and values of the new faith, and the old attractions of the sciences seemed to lose their erstwhile appeal, as is best seen in the writings of St. Augustine. It was only with the advent of the translators of the eleventh century or thereabout that the learning of the ancients returned to the Christian West, which then found itself in a position to resume the courageous efforts so long neglected.

But all was far from peace and joy even then. The renewed interest in the quest for science, as seen in the honors accorded the writings of Hippocrates, Aristotle, Theophrastus, Galen, and Celsus, in the biological area, and Ptolemy, Euclid, Aristotle, Vitruvius, Pliny, Hero, Pappus, Archimedes, etc., in the physical and mathematical fields, did not automatically bring with it a promise of inevitable advance. Indeed, for several centuries progress seemed to be slow, if not stopped.

The usual explanation for that apparently slow advance is well known. It is claimed that religious dogma filled the minds of men in those, as frequently described, dark centuries, that authoritarianism prevailed as a mode of thought, and that the habit of experimentation, testing, questioning, and verification was unknown and unwanted. It is asserted almost universally that Aristotle and Galen became the autocrats of the biological sciences, with Ptolemy reigning over astronomy and geography, and that contradicting any of these rulers was fraught with utmost danger. Only by challenging these church-sanctioned authorities could progress be made at all, and the challengers were presumably few but sufficiently bold to defy fierce persecution. Such were Vesalius and Harvey in biology, Copernicus and Galileo in astronomy and physics. By their efforts the ancients were dethroned, so that science could resume its forward march.

Like all false or incorrect theories, this one has a kernel of truth, or even a considerable dose of it, but it falls short nonetheless, in the form stated, of being accurate or helpful. We shall let the facts speak for themselves as to what is a proper evaluation of the nature of scientific progress, what may be the true causes of failure to advance, and how may a prolonged standstill ultimately come to an end. The present study can give some answers to these questions because it limits itself to an examination of scientific progress within a limited area, namely, the circulation of the blood and the role of respiration. We trace the growth of this area from the very earliest foundations in the writings of Aristotle and Galen, via the writings of Vesalius and Fabricius, to Harvey and a few who followed him, up to within a generation after his death. These authors are permitted to have their own says so that the reader may observe their modes of expression, their notions of evidence, their ways with challenge or acceptance of ideas, their attitudes to experimentation and authority, their notions of proof and truth, and above all, the tacit assumptions, values, beliefs, and conceptions in the realm of which they did their thinking.

The topic chosen happens to be pivotal to most life sciences, especially zoology, physiology, and medicine. The discoverer of the circulation, William Harvey, occupies an exalted position in the history of science, on a par with Edward Jenner, the founder of vaccination, Louis Pasteur, the discoverer of microbial infection and immunity, and Charles Darwin, the father of evolution. Moreover, Harvey's discovery came early in an era of upsurge of interest in modern science, and his achievement undoubtedly helped to usher it in.

Blood as a life-endowing fluid attracted attention even in primitive and early cultures. All scientific writers of ancient Greece were intrigued by it, although the modern student may well wonder how such a simple phenomenon as its flow could have escaped the keen eye or mind of a Galen or a Vesalius. But the fact that two such giants failed to discern the nature of the circulation should alone inform us that it was far from obvious. Further, if after the rediscovery of Galen's numerous works and Aristotle's *History of Animals* mankind had to wait close to five-hundred years for the appearance of William Harvey, then surely it must be concluded that the idea was not easy to come by. The culture was clearly cognizant of the problem, and admittedly no human group—no nation, race, or tribe—lacks capable intellects willing to grapple with the issues of which society is aware. It therefore seems reasonable to assume that what turned out to be the correct answer was difficult or impossible to find because of prevailing strong obstacles, blind spots, or distractions. A study of such hindrances and of the conditions finally abetting progress is bound to be enlightening to the student of science and its history. It is the aim of this volume to shed some light upon the complex process of scientific advancement and to guide the student in examining as many of its elements as possible.

2. ARISTOTLE

The History of Animals

[HISTORIA ANIMALIUM]

Now, as the nature of blood and the nature of the veins have all the appearance
of being primitive, we must discuss their
properties first of all, and all the more as
some previous writers have treated them
very unsatisfactorily. And the cause of the
ignorance thus manifested is the extreme
difficulty experienced in the way of observation. For in the dead bodies of animals
the nature of the chief veins is undiscov-
erable, owing to the fact that they collapse
at once when the blood leaves them; for
the blood pours out of the brain in a
stream, like liquid out of a vessel, since
there is no blood separately situated by
itself, except a little in the heart, but it is
all lodged in the veins. In *living* animals it
is impossible to inspect these parts, for of
their very nature they are situated inside
the body and out of sight. For this reason
anatomists who have carried on their investigations on dead bodies in the dissect-
ing-room have failed to discover the chief
roots of the veins, while those who have
narrowly inspected bodies of living men
reduced to extreme attenuation have ar-

From *Historia Animalium* (Volume IV of *The Works
of Aristotle*), translated by D. W. Thompson, Oxford
University Press, London, 1910, Book III, Sections
2, 3, 4, and 19.

rived at conclusions regarding the origin of the veins from the manifestations visible externally. Of these investigators, Syennesis, the physician of Cyprus, writes as follows:—

'The big veins run thus:—from the navel, across the loins, along the back, past the lung, in under the breasts; one from right to left, and the other from left to right; that from the left, through the liver to the kidney and the testicle, that from the right, to the spleen and kidney and testicle, and from thence to the penis.'

Diogenes of Apollonia writes thus:—

'The veins in man are as follows:—There are two veins pre-eminent in magnitude. These extend through the belly along the backbone, one to right, one to left; either one to the leg on its own side, and upwards to the head, past the collar bones, through the throat. From these, veins extend all over the body, from that on the right hand to the right side and from that on the left hand to the left side; the most important ones, two in number, to the heart in the region of the backbone; other two a little higher up through the chest in underneath the armpit, each to the hand on its own side: of these two, one being termed the vein *splenitis,* and the other the vein *hepatitis.* Each of the pair splits at its extremity; the one branches in the direction of the thumb and the other in the direction of the palm; and from these run off a number of minute veins branching off to the fingers and to all parts of the hand. Other veins, more minute, extend from the main veins; from that on the right towards the liver, from that on the left towards the spleen and the kidneys. The veins that run to the legs split at the juncture of the legs with the trunk and extend right down the thigh. The largest of these goes down the thigh at the back of it, and can be discerned and traced as a big one; the second one runs inside the thigh, not quite as big as the one just mentioned. After this they pass on along the knee to the shin and the foot (as the upper veins were described as passing towards the hands), and arrive at the sole of the foot, and from thence continue to the toes. Moreover, many delicate veins separate off from the great veins towards the stomach and towards the ribs.

. . . . .

'There is also another pair running on each side through the spinal marrow to the testicles, thin and delicate. There is, further, a pair running a little underneath the cuticle through the flesh to the kidneys, and these with men terminate at the testicle, and with women at the womb. These veins are termed the spermatic veins. The veins that leave the stomach are comparatively broad just as they leave; but they become gradually thinner, until they change over from right to left and from left to right.

'Blood is thickest when it is imbibed by the fleshy parts; when it is transmitted to the organs above-mentioned, it becomes thin, warm, and frothy.'

. . . . .

The above quotations sum up pretty well the statements of all previous writers. Furthermore there are some writers on Natural History who have not ventured to lay down the law in such precise terms as regards the veins, but who all alike agree in assigning the head and the brain as the starting-point of the veins. And in this opinion they are mistaken.

. . . . .

The heart in all animals has cavities inside it. In the case of the smaller animals even the largest of the chambers is scarcely discernible; the second larger is scarcely discernible in animals of medium size; but in the largest animals all three chambers are distinctly seen. In the heart then (with its pointed end directed frontwards, as has been observed) the largest of the three chambers is on the right-hand side and highest up; the least one is on the left-hand side; and the medium-sized one lies in betwixt the other two; and the largest one of the three chambers is a great deal larger than either of the two others. All three, however, are connected with passages leading in the direction of the lung, but all these communications are indistinctly discernible by reason of their minuteness, except one.

The great blood-vessel, then, is attached to the biggest of the three chambers, the one that lies uppermost and on the right-hand side; it then extends right through the chamber, coming out as blood-vessel again; just as though the cavity of the heart were a part of the vessel, in which the blood broadens its channel as a river that widens out in a lake. The aorta is attached to the middle chamber; only, by the way, it is connected with it by a much narrower pipe.

· · · · ·

And in like manner the parts of the lesser one of the two chief blood-vessels, designated the aorta, branch off, accompanying the branches from the big vein; only that, in regard to the aorta, the passages are less in size, and the branches very considerably less than are those of the great vein. So much for the veins as observed in the regions above the heart.

· · · · ·

There is no vessel that runs from the aorta into the liver or the spleen.

· · · · ·

And now to proceed to the consideration of the blood. In sanguineous animals blood is the most universal and the most indispensable part; and it is not an acquired or adventitious part, but it is a consubstantial part of all animals that are not corrupt or moribund. All blood is contained in a vascular system, to wit, the veins, and is found nowhere else, excepting in the heart. Blood is not sensitive to touch in any animal, any more than the excretions of the stomach; and the case is similar with the brain and the marrow. When flesh is lacerated, blood exudes, if the animal be alive and unless the flesh be gangrened. Blood in a healthy condition is naturally sweet to the taste, and red in colour; blood that deteriorates from natural decay or from disease is more or less black. Blood at its best, before it undergoes deterioration from either natural decay or from disease, is neither very thick nor very thin. In the living animal it is always liquid and warm, but, on issuing from the body, it coagulates in all cases except in the case of the deer, the roe, and the like animals; for, as a general rule, blood coagulates unless the fibers be extracted. Bull's blood is the quickest to coagulate.

· · · · ·

Blood beats or palpitates in the veins of all animals alike all over their bodies, and blood is the only liquid that permeates the entire frames of living animals, without exception and at all times, as long as life lasts. Blood is developed first of all in the heart of animals before the body is differentiated as a whole. If blood be removed or if it escape in any considerable quantity, animals fall into a faint or swoon; if it be removed or if it escape in an exceedingly large quantity they die. If the blood get exceedingly liquid, animals fall sick; for the blood then turns into something like ichor, or a liquid so thin that it at times has been known to exude through the pores like sweat. In some cases blood, when issuing from the veins, does not coagulate at all, or only here and there. Whilst animals are sleeping the blood is less abundantly supplied near the exterior surfaces, so that, if the sleeping creature be pricked with a pin, the blood does not issue as copiously as it would if the creature were awake. Blood is developed out of ichor by coction, and fat in like manner out of blood. If the blood get diseased, haemorrhoids may ensue in the nostril or at the anus, or the veins may become varicose. Blood, if it corrupt in the body, has a tendency to turn into pus, and pus may turn into a solid concretion.

Blood in the female differs from that in the male, for, supposing the male and female to be on a par as regards age and general health, the blood in the female is thicker and blacker than in the male;

· · · · ·

Women are seldom afflicted with varicose veins, with haemorrhoids, or with bleeding at the nose, and, if any of these maladies supervene, the menses are imperfectly discharged.

The First Account

It is only just that the story of man's discovery of the circulation of the blood begin with an excerpt from Aristotle's *History of Animals*. The book presents a detailed account of remarkable dissections and life histories of about 520 animals and the structures and interrelationships of all animals then known—their courtship, reproduction, development, diet, behavior, habitat, migration, adaptation, and even impact on man. It is a pioneering encyclopedia of zoology, gathered by a keen observer and philosopher at a time when that science had hardly emerged as such. It is a book that has to be read to be appreciated for its scope and contribution.

Aristotle (384–322 B.C.) views blood as one of the tissues, among which he enumerates muscle, bone, lymph, fiber, hair, secretions, some excretions, and sinew, which includes nerve. The home of all blood is in the veins, by which term Aristotle implies arteries as well. Whereas Hippocrates, who lived more than a century before him, distinguished arteries from veins by the thicknesses of their walls, Aristotle merely points out that some vessels, meaning arteries, are more sinewy than others. Credit for the definitive distinction between the two kinds of blood vessels must go to Herophilus, a native of Asia Minor, who lectured on anatomy and physiology at the renowned museum of Alexandria around 300 B.C.

We learn from Aristotle's text that many famous anatomists had published their dissections before the time of his work, including dissections of human cadavers. Of interest is Aristotle's comment that there still existed many gaps in the science to worry many of its devotees. There was considerable disagreement in the conclusions of the authorities, with Aristotle rejecting, for example, the view that the brain was the fountainhead of the veins. The aorta was well known and was so named because "even in dead bodies part of it is observed to be full of air." The reader will no doubt find Aristotle's description of the heart quite baffling. The translator of the text, D'Arcy Thompson, comments wisely: "The Aristotelian account of the vascular system is remarkable for its wealth of detail, for its great accuracy in many particulars, and for its extreme obscurity in others. It is so far true to nature that it is clear evidence of minute inquiry, but here and there so remote from fact as to suggest that these things once seen had been half-forgotten, or that superstition was in conflict with the results of observation."

Aristotle's bewildering description of the heart must be attributed to the innate complexity of that organ and the various vessels linked with it. Give even a large heart, such as that of a pig or cow, to any bright student as yet unfamiliar with it, and observe the initial confusion in his mind, which is prepared by all the conceptual knowledge available at present. Think, then, how the heart must have puzzled men of antiquity who could be guided by no ideas of any kind. The text conveys this confusion most eloquently.

Aristotle regards the heart as a way station for the great blood vessel, the vena cava, which presumably passes through it on its way to the aorta. The big vein "extends right through the chamber, coming out as blood-vessel again." It is "made of membrane of skin, while the aorta is narrower and very sinewy." But he also states: "These blood-vessels have their origins in the heart," meaning the aorta and vena cava. He regards the right auricle and ventricle as "the largest of the three chambers" that he claims to find in the heart. He keenly discerns that branches of the aorta "accompany . . . the branches from the big vein" and that the vein that enters the liver disappears in it. Alongside these observations, some of which are quite refined, one stumbles every now and then upon some obvious errors. But then Aristotle is fully aware of the difficulties and voices his concern on several occasions. Besides, one must not forget that the distribution of blood vessels may vary from individual to individual.

We should not judge too hastily Aristotle's loose comments on the nature of blood, most of which are, of course, wholly fanciful. The subject of blood had been embedded in an aura of mystery, rhetoric, and fable since oldest times. What should rather impress us is that he offers as many objective statements about it as he does. His general tone is factual and in the manner of modern description, in spite of the occasional superstitious inaccuracies and vagaries. All we may safely assert is that if a master observer and organizer like Aristotle acted thus, then the final goal could probably not have been reached any more easily by the human species.

3. GALEN

On Anatomical Procedures

[DE ANATOMICIS ADMINISTRATIONIBUS]

The most important organs for breathing are the lungs, heart, and thorax. Next after these are two kinds of arteries. One kind is distributed from the left ventricle of the heart throughout the body. These beat with the same rhythm as the heart. They all spring, as branches from a trunk, from the greatest artery [*aorta*]. Some call it by that very name 'greatest' (ME-GISTĒ), others simply 'the great' (ME-GALĒ), others 'the thick' (PACHEIA), and others 'the straight' (ORTHĒ). The second kind of artery is that which they call 'the rough' (TRACHEIA). This is a very large one in the neck [*trachea*] and has many offshoots [*bronchi*] throughout the lungs. At the upper end of this large neck artery lies a sort of head called the LARYNX. This is named by more modern anatomists 'the head of the bronchus,' because the trachea is not only 'rough' but also connected with the bronchi.

· · · · ·

That my account may be lucid, I shall now explain the names which we have to employ. As all designate the pulsating

From *Galen on Anatomical Procedures,* translated by C. Singer, Oxford University Press, London, 1956, Book VII (Heart, Lungs, and Arteries), pp. 172–200.

organ KARDIA [*heart*], so they call each pulsating vessel ARTERIA.

It is easy to discern the arteries throughout the body by their pulsation and by their continuity with the great artery. But it is impossible to discern by the senses the pulsation of those in the lungs [i.e. branches of the 'venous artery,' *pulmonary vein*]. In spite of this one might guess at [their nature] from their continuity with the left ventricle of the heart. Nevertheless, some think they have not only a suspicion, or a well-founded expectation, but exact knowledge of their activity. The two schools claim knowledge in different ways, arising from different opinions.

The one school, following Erasistratus, assumes that the arteries in the lungs [*pulmonary veins*] are empty of blood like the other arteries. They hold that at each diastole of the heart the PNEUMA is drawn through them out of the lungs [into the left ventricle] and by its passage the pulse is produced in all the arteries throughout the body. They are persuaded that the pulse is not produced in these [arteries] by their own action, as in that of the heart, but by their being filled with the PNEUMA passing through them. They say, too, that the heart, when it contracts, sends forth the PNEUMA to the arteries.

The other school thinks that the other arteries [in the body] as well as those in the lungs [i.e. branches of the 'venous artery,' *pulmonary vein*] contract and dilate by the same power as the heart. They say that the difference is that the power belongs by nature to the heart and is infused into the arteries from it.

According to the first school, if, on a living animal, you cut through all ribs on both sides and examine the lung [you will find that] so long as the rough arteries [i.e. bronchial tree] convey PNEUMA to the smooth arteries [*pulmonary veins*] that come from the heart, you will find a kind of pulse in them, but when they [i.e. the rough arteries] are empty there will be none.

According to the second school, while the animal lives not

only do the arteries in the moving part of the lungs go on pulsating but also those in the exposed part.

As for the received opinions of the experts, I have explained what consequences follow. But since in this work I am not concerned with passing judgment on opinions, but with the phenomena revealed by dissection, I shall try to guide you to the facts. Therefore make a straight incision in a downward direction along the length of the animal where the ribs are cartilaginous. With a single stroke of a large scalpel you can sever all the ribs below the first. Spare that rib for fear of the haemorrhage that might follow your wounding the vessels under it. If you have succeeded so far, strip off the membrane [i.e. visceral layer of *pleura*] from the lungs as fast as possible. Then with your fingers remove the flesh between the [pulmonary] vessels and lay them bare. Try to see and feel if any of the vessels in the lungs has a pulse. Anything you find with a pulse you may regard as an artery. But unless its movement be clearly distinguished you should not call a vessel an artery, whether it spring from the left ventricle or the right, whatever some of the anatomists may say. They differ from one another over this terminology, for some declare that the vessel springing from the left ventricle is an artery or vein, others that springing from the right. A better course is theirs who refuse to call either of these 'artery' or 'vein' simply, but modify this hasty ascription by calling them 'arterial vein' or 'venous artery.' In fact four names have been given to two vessels by anatomical experts.

I follow what I take to be the better view of those who call the vessel springing from the left ventricle of the heart 've-nous artery' [*pulmonary vein*] and that springing from the right ventricle 'arterial vein' [*pulmonary artery*]. I think it preferable (since we cannot distinguish them clearly by the pulse) to call the vessel containing PNEUMA an 'artery' but, since it has the covering of a vein, to add 'venous.' So to the other I give the name of 'vein' from its function, but since its substance is that of an artery, I add 'arterial.'

· · · · ·

It is now time to detail of what substance the vessels are made.

The veins throughout the body have come into being each with a single intrinsic coat, for the membrane that sometimes surrounds them is in contact with them only where they need to be bound to certain tissues or fixed firmly and protected. The arteries have two intrinsic coats, the outer [*tunica adventitia*] like that of the vein, the inner [*tunica media*] about five times as thick and harder. It consists of transverse fibres. The outer coat, like that of the veins, has longitudinal fibres, some slightly oblique, but none transverse. The inner, thick, hard tunic of the arteries has a woven sort of membrane on its inner surface, which can be seen in the large vessels. Some regard it as a third coat [*tunica intima*]. There is no fourth intrinsic coat but, like certain of the veins, some arteries have attached to and round them in places a delicate membrane which guards or fixes them firmly or binds them to the neighboring parts. The peritoneum does this to the arteries and veins, specially below the diaphragm, as does the membrane [*pleura*] in the region above which underlies the ribs within the thorax, as was told above.

What the arteries are throughout the body, such is that vessel from the right ventricle of the heart which branches throughout the lungs [*pulmonary artery*]. And what the veins are, such is the vessel from the left ventricle [*pulmonary vein*].

• • • • •

The muscles have uniform fibres, but not so the heart nor the proper coat of uterus or bladder. A careless glance will suggest that the muscle substance and the heart substance are alike (as are those of nerves, ligaments, and tendons), but the difference in these simple and primary bodies has been already discussed elsewhere, and will be again as needed. Nevertheless, that the substance of the heart differs in many respects from that of a muscle, has been well enough demonstrated, and its activity also testifies to this. For the movement of the heat is involuntary and ceaseless, so long as the animal survives, while that of the muscles is often suspended, and springs to activity in obedience to the animal's impulses.

All philosophers and physicians who are experts in natural

science (deinoi peri physin) agree that activities accord with the peculiarities of the substance. Therefore all parts of the same substance are active in the same way, even in animals that diverge in other characters, while in the same animals parts of different character have different activities. Thus every heart has the same activity, and so, too, every thorax and every pair of lungs, but the kidneys, bladder, liver, and stomach do not have the same [activity] as any of these or of each other. So the muscles do not have the same activity as the heart, for they do not have the same nature.

If heart and muscle be cooked together and eaten, differences in their taste will be found, just as with spleen, kidneys, lungs, liver, tongue, or any other organ. All differ in taste, touch, appearance, hardness, softness, density, and colour.

. . . . .

Moreover, they err as to the nature of the nerves. They think that the brain is like them in all its parts, except that some are more, and some less, soft. Through some nerves [the brain] transmits the power of sensation to the parts below, through others, voluntary movement. It is intelligible that all the nerves should have both these powers, but the soft are more suited for sensation, the hard for movement. Some of the strands from the same root divide into branches, some of which can be followed into muscles, others into other parts. This happens with the third cranial pair [*trigeminal*] and the sixth [IX + X + XI]. From the latter the heart receives a strand, for from it [*vagus*] not only heart and lungs, liver, stomach, mesentery, and intestines, but also all the muscles of the larynx and certain others receive branches.

Those who say that the heart is a [mere] muscle, notice nothing, not even that, had it lacked motor strands, as they think it does, it could neither move by volition, nor receive its pulsatory activity which must presumably have some cause. This, they must claim, is either a gift from the nerves or is inherent by nature in the organ. Now it does not come from the nerves, for all the organs that receive nerves would have shared in it and when they were severed the heart would not continue beating. But we see neither of these things happen.

Therefore the power of pulsation has its origin in the heart itself. It would not have arisen if the organ had had the same nature as the muscles throughout the whole animal. But the fact that the heart, removed from the thorax, can be seen to move for a considerable time is a definite indication that it does not need the nerves to perform its own function. Those who think the heart a muscle seem ignorant of these things and to have failed to notice that pulsation is of its essence, by the high virtue of some special element in its nature.

. . . . .

Now let us proceed to the particular parts that are the subject of this work, beginning from the 'auricles' of the heart. They are thus called from their resemblance to ears, for they grow on either side of the heart as ears on the head.

. . . . .

There are two 'auricles,' one by each of the vessels that brings in material—on the right, at the entry of [EMPHYSIS] the vein [*superior vena cava*] into the cavity of the heart; on the left, at that of the 'venous artery' [*pulmonary vein*]. When you lay open the 'auricles' the substance (SŌMA) of the heart will be visible, and each of the above-named orifices and then the valves (HYMENES) attached below the entries (EMPHYSEIS), three to the right cavity [*tricuspid valve*], two to the left [*mitral valve*].

. . . . .

Thus even very large structures in animals may escape notice by the inexperienced. What wonder that Aristotle, among his many anatomical errors, thinks that the heart in large animals has three cavities? It is not surprising that, lacking anatomical experience, he failed to find the parts, and he deserves to be forgiven. For where those who have given their whole life to this study, as Marinus, have made many mistakes, what are we to think happens to those who approach it without preparation, but deterred by a first failure abandon further attempt?

I call all gods to witness that I have often, on further examination, seen things I had completely missed before. Among them is the bone in the heart, for I learned from my teachers neither its position nor whether it be present in all animals.

• • • • •

You will see, if you lay bare the whole heart, the left ventricle extending to the very apex, and the right ending much below it, and often with an outline of its own. This [double apex] is seen in large animals like horses and oxen and camels, and still more in elephants, but sometimes even in small ones. Thus a man who was sacrificing a cock to the gods found a heart with two apexes. Thinking this a portent, he consulted the experts. By chance he met me and said that he had found two hearts in one animal. There were not two, as he thought, but the apex of the right ventricle had an outline of its own. Grasp this, then, thoroughly: that were an animal larger than an elephant or smaller than a lark, the structure of the heart would be similar, nay yet rather in appearance the same.

• • • • •

The orifice of the 'venous artery' [*pulmonary vein*] at the left ventricle (KOILIA) is single and on it are the valves opening inwards [*mitral*]. Yet it [i.e. the vessel] hardly remains one, but at once divides into four, each of which reaches a lobe of the lung.

• • • • •

After death the lungs are collapsed and small, there being a considerable space between them and the chest wall contrary to the condition in life. This will be considered after the discussion of the heart, for it remains to describe how to expose it while the animal is alive, without damaging the thoracic cavities [i.e. the *pleurae*].

• • • • •

Use a young animal so that you do not need large knives. It must be on its back, on a board of the kind that you see I have quantities at hand, both large and small, so that one may always be found to fit the animal. This board should have holes bored in it through which a thin cord or even a rope will easily pass. An assistant should be instructed, when the animal is on its back on the board, to pass cords round it, one round each limb and the ends of the cords through the holes below and tied together there. If the animal has long hair about the breast-bone, that should be removed.

This is the way to prepare the subject for dissection. Make a straight incision with a large lancet along the sternum downwards to the ensiform cartilage.

· · · · ·

When the heart is exposed, your task is to preserve all its functions unimpaired, as in fact they are, so that you can see the animal breathing and uttering cries and, if loosed from its bonds, running as before. Further, if you continue to compress the wound with ligatures, you will see it taking food if hungry, and drinking if thirsty. And what is strange in that? The slave of Maryllus, the mime-writer, whose heart was exposed, was cured and still lives [see below]. It is surely more likely that a non-rational brute, being less sensitive than a human being, will suffer nothing from such a wound.

· · · · ·

What then are the purposes of exposing the heart thus? First, that we may see clearly how it beats and whether it is in diastole or systole that it strikes the chest in the sternal region. Secondly, that, laying bare the great artery, as you have seen me exposing that in the groin, we may observe exactly whether it is contracted while the heart is in diastole and expanded when it is in systole, or if both [heart and artery] are expanded and contracted at the same time. Thirdly, by grasping the heart with the fingers—or with forceps as I habitually do since it readily escapes the fingers —we may see what sort of symptom is produced in the animal. And, moreover, to expose the error of those who say that such and such symptoms seize on the animal if one ligates the large artery or, as some say, the 'venous artery' [*pulmonary vein*] running into the lungs. . . .

I found by experience that this was always said by those who could not expose the heart without perforation but who, under pressure, immediately perforated the thorax, saying that the operation was difficult; and that it was for this reason that they had postponed it, for [they said] had they exposed it, they would have put the ligature round it and demonstrated clearly what they promised.

In contrast to them, what I promise I perform. For I expose the heart easily without damage to any of the membranes partitioning the cavity of the thorax. Then I ask them to put the ligature round the vessels springing from the heart. Under compulsion, without effecting anything, they get so far as to tear apart some of the membranes and make a perforation. At that point they say they ought not to make any further attempt. But again I speedily expose the heart in another animal for them, and present this to them, and force them to make another attempt, until they are put to shame over their impudent pretences.

．　．　．　．　．

All this will be clear to you at once when [the heart] is exposed. As time goes on, the movements of each ventricle become brief, long pauses intervening, and also there becomes apparent the diastole of the right ventricle, accomplishing [its function] according to its own nature, as you will see particularly when those [parts] approach immobility. For in each [ventricle] the apex stops moving first and then the part next to it, and so on until the bases only are left still moving. When even these have stopped, an ill-defined and short movement at long intervals is still seen in the 'auricles.' The cause of this phenomenon we must investigate at leisure, for it would seem natural (EULOGON) that its appendages should move longer than the heart itself. But here it is not our aim to examine causes but observed anatomical phenomena only.

．　．　．　．　．

For those who vivisect almost all that is necessary and useful has been said concerning the heart. It would be better now to turn to the phenomena of the thorax and lungs. But since some, talking impudent nonsense, openly promise to show that the arteries are empty of blood, one giving the lie to the other on actual observations, I too must spend time on this topic.

One of them was always promising to exhibit the great artery empty of blood, but never did so. When some ardent youths brought animals to him and challenged him to the test, he declared he would not make it without a fee. They laid down at once a thousand drachmae for him to pocket should he succeed. In his embarrassment he made many twists and turns, but, under pressure from all present, mustered courage to take a lancet and cut along the left side of the thorax especially, at the point where, he thought, the aorta should become visible. He proved so little practised in dissection that he cut on to the bone!

Another of the same gang (CHOROS) made his cut onto the bone across the intercostal region, and straightaway severed artery and vein. Thus the fellow incurred the ridicule of the youths who had deposited the stakes with the assembled spectators. The youths themselves now carried out what the last had promised, making their incision as they had seen me, without damaging any vessels. Moreover, they quickly applied two ligatures, one immediately beyond the point where the aorta rises from the heart, the other where it reaches the spine. Thus, as the impudent fellow had promised, after the death of the animal it might be seen whether this stretch of the artery between the ligatures were empty of blood. When it was found far from empty, they said that an irruption had taken place into it when the ligatures were applied, as if someone else and not they themselves had undertaken to do the operation, though they were without the necessary experience and were incapable of applying the ligatures faster than others. For they did not even know that an artery and vein follow the lower border of each rib.

· · · · ·

We may recall yet another effort, that of a pompous septuagenarian who claimed that he would demonstrate an artery empty of blood. The animal must be one that can be readily skinned, as a sheep, ox, or goat. The incision must be made at some point where a large artery lies just beneath the skin. The artery must have the skin removed all round and bared of the surrounding tissues so that it stand free. The cut in the skin must be protected and, after six or seven days, its edges opened and two ligatures put round the artery, as far apart as possible. When the part between were cut out it would then, he said, be found empty. This old fellow never dared to make his experiment himself, but we did so for him as soon as we heard of it. We tried it on a goat, on kine, and on sheep, as the old man had directed. We then invited him to wake up and see for himself, once and for all, and be convicted of the error of what had appeared to him in a mere dream.

Moreover, not long since another fellow gave a totally false account of an experiment described by me in my book *An in arteriis natura sanguis contineatur*. Those who had observed my experiment were astonished at his temerity and asked him if he had ever performed it himself or merely relied on hearsay. He replied that he had performed it often. So they brought a goat and tried to force him to demonstrate it. He declined because, of course, he did not know how. They then demonstrated to the onlooker that the actual phenomenon was different [from what he said] and thus ended his absurd claims.

The method of experiment is as follows. Of the large arteries near the skin, expose one, such as that by the groin, which is the one that I habitually use for the operation. Ligature it above and compress the artery itself with the fingers of the left hand, choosing as great a length as possible from the ligature devoid of a large branch. Then make in its wall a straight incision long enough for you to insert a tube between the ligature and the fingers. (Have ready a tube of a finger's length, such as a writing quill, or a bronze pipe made for the purpose.) Obviously there will be no haemorrhage from the severed artery since the upper part, whence comes the blood, is stopped by the ligature, while the lower part no longer pulsates because of the ligature and because it is compressed by the fingers. Hence you can at your leisure insert the tube into the artery through the incision in its wall, and then ligate artery and quill with fine linen thread. (Take care that no part of the tube go [too far] beyond the incision of the artery, and that the quill will be of a calibre that the arterial coat does not lie slack on it, for we want it to remain in place, neither running up beyond the division in the artery, nor down it.) This done, loosen the ligature [first made] and, as a precaution, alter the position of the fingers with which you were compressing the artery, to the part round the quill. If the quill be tight and well ligated, there is no need to control it, and you can observe the uninterrupted part of the artery above the tube still pulsating as before and the lower part quite pulseless.

This then is what is actually observed. Erasistratus, however, gave an opposite account, saying that the part below the quill is seen moving. So great is the temerity of those who make rash assertions without observing.

On the Functions of Parts of the Human Body

[DE USU PARTIUM CORPORIS HUMANI]

Respiration in animals, as we have seen, exists for the sake of the heart, which requires the substance of the air, and scorched by heat desires most strongly the coolness thus provided. Penetrating with its cooling virtue, the air refreshes the heart; it then leaves it, dragging along with it the effervescent particles of a nature burnt and sooty. It is for this reason that the heart has a double movement in accordance with the conditions which operate in a reversible manner, because it draws in as it dilates and empties itself in contracting. Consider to begin with, in this connection, the providence of nature. Since it was advantageous for man to possess a voice, and sound to be produced must necessarily have air, she has contrived to supply it with all the air which otherwise would have been expired without profit or use.

· · · · ·

The heart being like the hearth and the

From *Opera Omnia of Claudius Galen,* edited by C. G. Kühn, Car. Cnoblochii, Leipzig, 1821–33, Volumes III and IV, and *Oeuvres Anatomiques, Physiologiques et Médicales de Galien,* translated by C. Daremberg, J. B. Baillière, Paris, 1854, Libri XVII, Book VI (The Organs of Respiration), Chapters 1–18, translated by M. Graubard.

source of the innate heat that vitalizes the animal, all its parts share in the execution of that major task, which maintains the life of the entire animal. These parts are the opening of the two vessels situated in the left cavity which doctors call as a rule the pneumatic cavity [the ventricle]. In effect, through the smaller of these orifices [the mitral or bicuspid or left auriculoventricular valve] the heart connects with the arteries of the lung, and through the bigger one [aortic orifice] with all the arteries that ramify through the body of the animal. Less vital are the orifices of the other cavity, called the blood cavity, although their importance surpasses that of some other parts of the heart, since one [the tricuspid or right auriculoventricular valve] brings the blood to the heart, while the other [the orifice of the pulmonary artery—the arterial vein] conducts it to the lung.

· · · · ·

In dispatching to the lung the nourishment which it draws from the liver, the heart appears to repay it in kind and recompense it for the air with which the lung honors it. The lung does in fact require nourishment. It would indeed be of no advantage for the blood to get to the lung directly from the vena cava, even though it flows close to it and touches it, but, to feed it properly, nature had to create a new kind of vessel which in no way resembles the vena cava and to provide this vessel with a membranous flap [the sigmoid valves of the pulmonary artery], the kind it indeed possesses. And this changed arrangement could be effected by no other organ but the heart. Nature, so wise under all conditions, which has not produced in any animal a single detail in vain or by sheer chance, acted as wisely with regard to the lung. She interchanged the tunics of the vessels, giving to the vein that of an artery and to the artery that of a vein. In all the other bodily regions where the dimensions of the artery and vein are the same, the tunics differ in thickness. There exists between them a significant difference, and Herophilus seems to have judged correctly in asserting that the thickness of an artery is six times that of a vein. Of all the organs in all the bodily parts, it is only the lung whose artery [the pulmonary vein] has the tunics of a vein, and the vein [the pulmonary artery] the tunics of an artery.

. . . . . .

It is of advantage to the animal that within its body the blood be enclosed in a tunic that is thin and porous, and that the pneuma be contained in one that is thick and compact; this is a matter requiring no elaborate explanations. It is sufficient to recall the natures of the two substances: the blood is thick, heavy and slow to move, while the pneuma is thin, light and quick of movement; it might justly be feared that the pneuma would all too readily be dissipated if it were not confined by thick, dense, and perfectly compact walls. The opposite must be said of the blood: if the enveloping wall were not thin and porous, it could hardly distribute itself to the neighboring parts and all its usefulness would be for nought. With such foresight indeed has the Creator fashioned the walls of the two kinds of vessels in accordance with their contents to prevent the premature dispersion of the pneuma and to overcome the excessive sluggishness of the blood.

But why did he fail to give the vein of the lung the customary thin wall and to the artery the usual thick one? There, too, as everywhere else, the pneuma is tenuous and light and needs to be enclosed; the blood on the contrary is thick and heavy and needs to be distributed to all parts of the lung, which demands nourishment more ample than the other parts of the animal, in view of the incessant agitation of this organ and the excessive heat which is communicated to it by the adjacent heart with its continuous motion. You admire no doubt the foresight of the artist.

. . . . .

When the thorax, on the other hand, dilates, the lung follows suit with the chest as a whole, as in inspiration. But neither in inspiration nor in expiration do the veins undergo the same amount of dilation as the arteries because they are not assigned the same function. The latter, hollowed out by nature to receive the pneuma, must readily be filled up during the inspiration and in turn quickly emptied during expiration and the production of the voice. Since the veins serve as reservoirs of nourishment, they need not dilate with inspiration nor contract with expiration. It would therefore be reasonable to provide the ones [pulmonary veins] with a soft vestment and the others [pulmonary arteries] with a tough one, since it is desirable that the former obey promptly the double motion of the thorax and the latter be indifferent to it. Since we have demonstrated elsewhere that the body is nourished by the blood it draws through the walls of the vessels, the lung may therefore conceivably run the risk of lacking a nutritive source in view of the fact that the tunic of its vein [pulmonary artery] is too thick.

· · · · ·

This is not the sole reason why the lung should preferably be nourished by the heart; another reason is, as we have promised to explain at the beginning of this chapter, that the lung has to be provided with veins possessing the tunics of arteries, and with membranous flaps, neither of which could be generated by the vena cava. Of these two, the first, that is, the necessity for thicker tunics, has already been demonstrated. Let us then pass on to the second point, which is that it is most fitting for the opening of the arterial vein, the tricuspid valve, to be provided with membranes of the shape and size that it happens to possess. Although the vessel was fashioned very thick and strong so as not to stretch or contract with ease, it is not endowed with such firm resistance as not to be overpowered by the energetic, grand, impetuous action of an organ like the thorax, especially during a deep inspiration, or when we speak aloud, or in any other way when we exercise the thorax all over by working actively with all the chest muscles. In none of these circumstances are the branches of the vein exempt from compression and contraction. If then the thorax be compressed and squeezed, the blood will readily penetrate all the branches, return next to the first opening, and be carried backward. A triple inconvenience will result; to begin with the blood will execute uselessly and to no purpose this double trip. When the lung expands, the blood flows and fills all the lung's veins; upon contracture it functions like a reflux that moves without end like the ebb and flow of straits, a reflux which gives to the blood a movement to and fro which would not be propitious to it. That unpleasantness is perhaps of little account; but the disturbance which results to the respiration is not of a minor nature. If it were most desirable for the greatest possible quantity of air to be drawn in with each act of inspiration, and correspondingly expelled with each expiration, this function could not be performed if the arteries did not contract and become compressed to the utmost. The more the action of the veins approaches that of the arteries, the more they disturb and confound the course of movement of the arteries [by compressing them]. One sees then how upset the total effect of respiration would be by the dilation and constriction of the nutritive channels, the veins. Their complete repose is essential, and the effect should be as if they did not exist and did not occupy any space in the chest where respiratory organs dilate and constrict.

• • • • •

A third inconvenience would accompany the backflow of blood during exhalation if our Creator had not conceived the valves. What these membranes are and how they prevent the backwash of blood you will soon clearly understand. I am now going to explain how prejudicial their absence would be to the animal; give me then your attention and I will base my discourse upon a proof already given.

In the entire body the arteries come together with the veins and exchange air and blood through extremely fine, invisible orifices. If the great mouth of the arterial vein [the tricuspid valve] would always remain open, if nature had not invented a way of opening and closing it alternately at the right moments, blood would never get through the invisible and minute passages of the arteries [into them] when the chest contracted. Not every substance has the same tendency to be attracted or rejected by various parts of the body. If a light substance, more readily than a heavy one, is attracted by the expansion of an organ and rejected by its contraction, then that which flows through a large duct is more easily attracted and correspondingly more easily returned than that which travels in a narrow one. When the thorax contracts, the arteries of the lung having the walls of veins [the pulmonary veins] are pressed and driven within on all sides and with force; they squeeze out the pneuma contained in them, exchanging it instantaneously for the particles of blood, which they absorb through the small ducts, an event which could never have been possible if the blood could retrace its steps or its path through the grand opening [tricuspid valve]. In reality, when the vein [pulmonary artery] is compressed on all sides, the blood, finding that very passage closed to it, penetrates in tiny droplets the small arterial branchings.

. . . . . .

The more the thorax tries to discharge the blood with violence, the more tightly do the flaps [of the valve] close the aperture. Inserted circularly from within outward, and embracing the entire circumference, they compose, perfect in form and size, simultaneously stretched and hardened, a firm wall that obstructs the opening. But overturned by the flow that operates from within [the right ventricle] outward and thrown against the walls of the vein [pulmonary artery], they offer to the flux an easy passage across the orifice, which opens and dilates considerably. When on the other hand the current flows oppositely from outside inward, it comes up against the membranes and presses one against the other, thus forming a well-closed gate.

At all the mouths of vessels that issue from the heart are to be found these membranous flaps that fall one toward the other and are so well set up that when they simultaneously harden and stretch they shut the opening tight. All of them have a common purpose, which is to oppose the return of the fluid; yet each has its specific task: the ones help push out the fluid from the heart in such a way that it is prevented from re-entering, while the others help bring it in and prevent it from leaving. Nature did not wish to impose upon the heart useless labors, condemning it to send blood to a part from which it were better withheld, and on the contrary, to draw it away from a region to which it should be sent.

. . . . .

Let us now proceed with the explanations which follow from what has been stated above, and which we have deferred till now. The openings of the heart are four in number. Three of them have three valve membranes, and the venous artery [the mitral valve, which Galen considers as belonging to the pulmonary veins] has two only. All arise from the orifices themselves; but emerging from there, some protrude into the ventricles of the heart in a manner to be there attached by strong ligaments [chordae tendineae]; others are turned outward, toward the place where the two vessels arise from the heart. There exist at the arterial vein [pulmonary artery], which as we said nourishes the lung, three membranes, hung from inside outward, and called because of their shape sigmoid by those who have practiced dissection with care. At the vein which conveys the blood [right auricle], there are also to be found three membranes turned from outside inward [tricuspid valve], but surpassing the preceding ones in thickness, strength, and beauty.

. . . . .

It is reasonable that vessels which convey material to the heart be equipped with large and strong valves, and that these be less firm in vessels which expel materials. I shall attempt to demonstrate that fact as well as other means employed by nature to attract or expel materials. It is difficult, even on observing various parts, to explain clearly these things; but without seeing them it is surely impossible. It is necessary to endeavor nonetheless to gain as clear an understanding of these matters as possible. The membranes oriented from the outside inward, which as we said are large and firm, are all of them attached at their bases to the heart proper and supported by solid ligaments. When the heart dilates, each of these ligaments, stretched by the pull of the organ, tugs at it and, so to speak, folds over the membrane on the very body of this organ. All the three membranes are thus folded over circularly on the heart wall, the orifices of the vessel are opened, and the heart draws easily through the large aperture the fluid contained in the vessels. Through this movement of dilation, the heart attracts toward itself the fluid and the vessel itself, which it draws in and traps by means of the membranes. It is not possible, in fact, that as the membranes are attracted by the heart, the vessel itself, which is attached to them, is not affected by the attraction. Also, with each dilating motion performed by the heart, the membranes, pulled by the ligament, are lowered into the very cavity of the heart, and when these are arranged circularly backward [downward], the orifice opens simultaneously as the vessels are drawn by the membranes into the heart; the materials contained within them then penetrate without hindrance into the cavity of that organ, since nothing stands in the way; on the contrary, the causes capable of accelerating the displacement of the fluid conspire to aid this advance. Material that changes places must be either attracted, thrust by some force, or driven. These three modes cooperate in the movements of materials when the heart dilates. The heart attracts the material, the auricles originally put there propel it, the vessels drive it. The principle of movement shared by all these parts resides in the very dilation of the heart itself.

The auricles, fibrous and hollow overgrowths placed in front of the openings, are usually slack and therefore empty; but when the heart dilates, they stretch and contract like the valves, thus compressing their contents and pushing them into the heart. As the orifices of the vessels themselves follow suit and are forcefully attracted inside the heart, they convey the material pushed forth by the auricles. The heart itself, endowed with all the attractive faculties imaginable, rapidly engulfs within the depths of its cavities the conveyed materials which it seizes and breathes in, so to say. In fact, whether you choose as your object of comparison bellows distended by the smiths that swell with the air they suck in, you will recognize that the same power exists to a greater degree in the heart; or if you compare it to the flame of lamps that suck up the oil, you will agree that this faculty is not lacking in the heart-source of all the natural heat; or again to the stone of Hercules, the lodestone, which attracts iron because of the affinity of the magnet for the metal (you will find that the heart also posssesses that attractive faculty).

What is more appropriate to the heart than the air that refreshes it? What is more useful than blood to serve as nourishment? It would seem that the heart might break one of its vessels in making use all at once of its powers of attraction, if the Creator of man had not, to prevent possible mischance, conceived for this situation an admirable device by placing in front of each orifice aiding the conveyance of the stuff, a peculiar cavity in the form of a reservoir for nourishment, so that the vessel runs no risk of being ruptured, should the heart attract with a sudden pull, because its narrowness does not permit it to furnish fully all that the organ demands. Fill a vessel with air, then empty it by sucking out the air with the mouth through the opening, and you will break it if you use violence. The same applies to the heart, which must needs fill rapidly its cavity, which is considerably greater than the capacity of the two vessels combined and which would surely rupture if it drew in the blood with vehemence, were it not provided with a cavity in front, such as in fact exists to serve its needs in the form of the two auricles.

· · · · ·

As to the valves. Those that belong to the vessels responsible for conveying materials [to the heart] should the more so surpass in strength and beauty those that belong to the vessels charged with carrying the stuff onward, since the dilating movement requires more strength than contraction. The heart, in fact, must exert itself more in attracting through its dilation than in expelling through its contraction. These three membranes, placed at each orifice for its closing and opening with exactness and speed, form an admirable testimony of the providence of nature.

· · · · ·

It is therefore with reason that a single orifice, the one of the venous artery [pulmonary vein, i.e., the mitral valve], alone has two wings. It alone, in fact, stands to gain an advantage by not being tightly closed, since it alone, by design, has the job of permitting passage from the heart to the lung to the fuliginous residues which the natural heat of the organ necessarily accumulates as it produces them in the course of action.

. . . . . .

The anastomoses of the arteries with the veins were not created by nature uselessly or in vain, but in order that the purpose of the respiration, or pulsations, be distributed not only to the heart and arteries, but also to the veins. We have already indicated what kind of purpose these serve. These ideas suffice for the needs of this work. We have spoken not long before of the necessity for all the organs of the body not to receive the same nourishment; that necessity demonstrates the utility of the difference among the vessels. If there were only one kind of vessel for the blood, all the parts of the body would be nourished by one and the same kind of aliment. Could there be anything more unreasonable or absurd than to imagine that the liver, for example, the heaviest and thickest of the visceral organs, requires for its nourishment the same blood as the lung, the most porous and the lightest bodily organ?

Also, what need did nature have for providing the animal body not only with arteries but also with veins? It is for this reason that the liver is nourished by the veins alone, veins extremely fine and porous, and the lung, conversely, is fed by arteries. The vessels destined to feed it resemble in fact arteries, as we have stated above. So much the more should we admire the foresight of nature, which created vessels of two kinds that anastomose with each other, and which need, above all, renders possible communication between the cavities of the heart, as we have already shown. At this point, in fact, we do not intend to show that this has taken place in the animal body, but why it has taken place. Just as the establishment of a fact precedes understanding the reason for that fact, as Aristotle says, it is similarly impossible to establish purposes without first recalling the functions.

The tiny pores which appear above all toward the middle of the partition between the cavities of the heart [the ventricles] were created with an eye to the communication of which we have spoken above, because among the other common needs indicated, it is of importance that the blood of the veins pass, thoroughly worked over, into the arteries, in precisely the manner in which the veins do it to the arteries and the stomach to the veins; and it is not altogether unreasonable to imagine that the vital pneuma, if it is true that such exists, is an exhalation of the blood, provided the blood is pure. We have already established that proposition. For our present discussion we need merely indicate that there is a purpose to the fact that the arteries contain a pure and light blood, since it is destined to sustain [assimilate] the vital air.

. . . . .

Since the substance composing the heart proper is heavy and dense and requires a heavy aliment, it is nourished by the blood of the vena cava before that vessel joins the heart. In fact, on arrival in this organ it must become warm, light and subtle. For this reason it makes sense on all counts, although the idea seems strange to some people, that the heart should furnish nourishment to the lung but fail to feed itself. The fact is the lung needs thin and vaporous blood, while the heart does not.

. . . . .

One artery and one vein encircle the entire substance of the heart, but no nerve seems to penetrate that tissue, no more than that of the liver, kidney, or spleen. Only the pericardium, the heart's envelope, seems to receive branches of small nerves; these divide and send some visible threads to obviously implant themselves in the heart proper, at least in the case of the large animals.

On the Natural Faculties

[PERI PHYSIKON DYNAMEON]

Seeing that all parts have the faculty of attracting what is suitable or well-disposed and of eliminating what is troublesome or irritating, it is not surprising that opposite movements should occur in them consecutively—as may be clearly seen in the case of the heart, in the various arteries, in the thorax and lungs. In all these the active movements of the organs and therewith the passive movements of [their contained] matters may be seen taking place almost every second in opposite directions. Now you are not astonished when the trachea-artery alternately draws air into the lungs and gives it out, and when the nostrils and the whole mouth act similarly; nor do you think it strange or paradoxical that the air is dismissed through the very channel by which it was admitted just before. Do you, then, feel a difficulty in the case of the veins which pass down from the liver into the stomach and intestines, and do you think it strange that nutriment should at once be yielded up to the liver and drawn back from it into the stomach by the same

From *On the Natural Faculties,* translated by A. J. Book III (Nerves, Veins, and Arteries of Hand and Foot), pp. 303–23. Reprinted by permission of the publisher and the Loeb Classical Library.

veins? You must define what you mean by this expression "at once." If you mean "at the same time" this is not what we ourselves say; for just as we take in a breath at one moment and give it out again at another, so at one time the liver draws nutrition from the stomach, and at another the stomach from the liver. But if your expression "at once" means that in one and the same animal a single organ subserves the transport of matter in opposite directions, and if it is this which disturbs you, consider inspiration and expiration. For of course these also take place through the same organs, albeit they differ in their manner of movement, and in the way in which the matter is conveyed through them.

. . . . .

For, as has already been said, speaking generally, everything has the power at different times of attracting from and of adding to everything else. What happens is just as if you might imagine a number of animals helping themselves at will to a plentiful common stock of food; some will naturally be eating when others have stopped, some will be on the point of stopping when others are beginning, some eating together, and others in succession. Yes, by Zeus! and one will often be plundering another, if he be in need while the other has an abundant supply ready to hand. Thus it is in no way surprising that matter should make its way back from the outer surface of the body to the interior, or should be carried from the liver and spleen into the stomach by the same vessels by which it was carried in the reverse direction.

In the case of the arteries this is clear enough, as also in the case of the heart, thorax, and lungs; for, since all of these dilate and contract alernately, it must needs be that matter is subsequently discharged back into the parts from which it was previously drawn. Now Nature foresaw this necessity, and provided the cardiac openings of the vessels with membranous attachments, to prevent their contents from being carried backwards. . . .

And further, it has been shown in other treatises that all the arteries possess a power which derives from the heart, and by virtue of which they dilate and contract.

Put together, therefore, the two facts—that the arteries have this motion, and that everything, when it dilates, draws neighboring matter into itself—and you will find nothing strange in the fact that those arteries that reach the skin draw in the outer air when they dilate, while those which anastomose at any point with the veins attract the thinnest and most vaporous part of the blood which these contain, and as for those arteries which are near the heart, it is on the heart itself that they exert their traction. For, by virtue of the tendency by which a vacuum becomes refilled, the lightest and thinnest part obeys the tendency before that which is heavier and thicker. Now the lightest and thinnest of anything in the body is firstly pneuma, secondly vapour, and in the third place that part of the blood which has been accurately elaborated and refined.

These, then, are what the arteries draw into themselves on every side; those arteries which reach the skin draw in the outer air (this being near them and one of the lightest of things); as to the other arteries, those which pass up from the heart into the neck, and that which lies along the spine, as also such arteries as are near these—draw mostly from the heart itself; and those which are further from the heart and skin necessarily draw the lightest part of the blood out of the veins. So also the traction exercised by the diastole of the arteries which go to the stomach and intestines takes place at the expense of the heart itself and the numerous veins in its neighborhood; for these arteries cannot get anything worth speaking of from the thick heavy nutriment contained in the intestines and stomach, since they first become filled with lighter elements. For if you let down a tube into a vessel full of water and sand, and suck the air out of the tube with your mouth, the sand cannot come up to you before the water, for in accordance with the principle of the refilling of a vacuum the lighter matter is always the first to succeed to the evacuation.

· · · · · ·

Now, apart from what has been said, the following is sufficient proof that something is taken over from the veins into the arteries. If you will kill an animal by cutting through a number of its large arteries, you will find the veins becoming empty along with the arteries: now, this could never occur if there were not anastomoses between them. Similarly, also, in the heart itself, the thinnest portion of the blood is drawn from the right ventricle into the left, owing to there being perforations in the septum between them: these can be seen for a great part [of their length]; they are like a kind of fossae [pits] with wide mouths, and they get constantly narrower; it is not possible, however, actually to observe their extreme terminations, owing both to the smallness of these and to the fact that when the animal is dead all the parts are chilled and shrunken. Here, too, however, our argument, starting from the principle that nothing is done by Nature in vain, discovers these anastomoses between the ventricles of the heart; for it could not be at random and by chance that there occurred fossae ending thus in narrow terminations.

And secondly [the presence of these anastomoses has been assumed] from the fact that, of the two orifices in the right ventricle, the one conducting blood in and the other out, the former is much the larger. For, the fact that the insertion of the vena cava into the heart is larger than the vein which is inserted into the lungs suggests that not all the blood which the vena cava gives to the heart is driven away again from the heart to the lungs. Nor can it be said that any of the blood is expended in the nourishment of the actual body of the heart, since there is another vein which breaks up in it and which does not take its origin nor get its share of blood from the heart itself. And even if a certain amount is so expended, still the vein leading to the lungs is not to such a slight extent smaller than that inserted into the heart as to make it likely that the blood is used as nutriment for the heart: the disparity is much too great for such an explanation. It is, therefore, clear that something is taken over into the left ventricle.

Moreover, of the two vessels connected with it, that which brings pneuma into it from the lungs is much smaller than the great outgrowing artery from which the arteries all over the body originate; this would suggest that it not merely gets pneuma from the lungs, but that it also gets blood from the right ventricle through the anastomoses mentioned.

Galen on the Functions of Blood

No one reading the preceding excerpts can help being impressed with their author's stature as an experimentalist and thinker. Galen was regarded throughout medieval times, that is, from the revival of learning within the Christian world, as the greatest physiologist, biological experimentalist, and physician in antiquity. His reputation was well deserved, as even these sketchy citations fully prove. Though selected for the purpose of presenting Galen's views on blood, they speak eloquently of his deep respect for data, his skill in experimentation, and his logical reasoning. They also bear testimony that he observed, evaluated, and reasoned on the basis of hypotheses, principles, and hidden assumptions, which is precisely what scientists do today.

Galen was born in the year 130 A.D. in the city of Pergamon, in Asia Minor, famous as a seat of learning and the home of a widely renowned medical temple, or Asclepion, a center of healing known throughout the empire. Since about 260 years before Galen's birth, Pergamon had been under Roman rule, and Galen's education, as well as his subsequent travels and activities, were representative of the Greco-Roman culture of his day. He studied anatomy as a young man with a well-known master, became an independent investigator, and then went to the great city of Alexandria for further anatomical and medical studies. He returned to his native city, where he became physician to the temple gladiators performing in municipal or religious contests. He moved next to Rome, where he pursued a successful private practice and engaged in heated debates with medical leaders who disagreed with him. After leaving Rome for a while, he returned as court physician to the wise emperor Marcus Aurelius and as tutor to his far different son, Commodus. Galen died in his home town at the age of seventy, in 200 A.D. He was the author of many treatises and voluminous works dealing with anatomy, physiology, medicine, and philosophy. He loved controversy and was frequently harsher toward his opponents than the needs of the argument warranted.

The first excerpt gives a fair idea of Galen's thoroughness and craftsmanship as an anatomist. Note the precision in his anatomical dissections. His descriptions are crisp, clear, and specific, indicative of absolute familiarity and sureness of hand. Could anyone reading this selection take seriously the fable occasionally encountered that "the Greeks shunned experimentation"?

As the text reveals, there already were in existence two sophisticated schools of thought on the nature of the pulse and the motion of the blood. According to Erasistratus, the heart draws in pneuma from the lung at diastole and beats by its "own action." Arteries do not have that power but yield a pulse due to the contraction of the heart as the pneuma passes through them. An opposing school held that arteries are contracted and dilated by a power flowing into them from the heart. The conflict seemed more significant then than it does now. Galen, on his part, prefers to stick to dissection in this anatomical work and asserts that he will refrain from taking sides on this vital issue.

The term *pneuma* in Greek is defined as air, vapor, or spirit. As employed by Erasistratus, Galen, and other physiologists, it meant the air, or airy or spiry principle, inspired by the lungs. According to Galen, it could also enter the arteries through terminal skin orifices. It commingled or combined with arterial blood either directly or in some unknown, subtle manner and rendered it lighter, hotter, purer, "more golden," and thinner than venous blood. The latter Galen regarded as thick and turbid. That he noted the difference in color between the two bloods is interesting, particularly since he stated* in Book VI, Chapter 4, of his *On the Opinions of Hippocrates and Plato,* "For the blood is the same, which is contained both in the right ventricle of the heart and in all the veins throughout the whole animal, and it corresponds to that which is held in all the arteries and which exists in the left ventricle."

On rare occasions Galen uses the term pneuma to designate specific powers or functions. Thus in the same work he expands the view that the human brain, the organ of thought, houses a divine soul containing the *psychic pneuma*. The brain with its pneuma is the fount of nerves, which conduct sensations and generate voluntary impulses. The brain is nourished by the breath and the blood supply of the rete mirabile, the fine network of blood vessels at its

---

* L. G. Wilson, "Erasistratus, Galen and the 'Pneuma,'" *Bull. Hist. Med.,* **33,** 314 (1959).

base. On the other hand, passion issues from the heart, in the left ventricle of which operates the vital pneuma, which is also found in the arteries. Only once in his voluminous writings does Galen mention another kind of spirit. In his *Method of Treatment*, Book XII, Chapter 5, he says,[*] "And if there also is a natural spirit, this again should be contained in the liver and the veins." Concerning the pneuma of the lungs, heart, and arteries, he is most specific. In his *Whether Blood Is Contained in the Arteries in Nature*, he asserts, "But the pneuma which is enclosed in the arteries is not thinner than the surrounding air, as its origin indicates. For it arises, in the opinion of Erasistratus, from the air surrounding us, which he summons into the body to those first arteries which are in the lung, thereupon from them to the heart and to the others." In his intricate and numerous argumentations, Galen sometimes speaks of pneuma as present even in the right ventricle and veins. Not knowing precisely what happens to the venous blood there, he relies on the catchall word pneuma. His failure to utilize the term "natural spirit" frequently and consistently is no doubt due to his inability to conceive of a special process occurring in the right ventricle, because no activity is apparent.

That pneuma referred to air, spirit, and function interchangeably is not surprising. Although the ancients knew that air was a substance having weight and capable of flowing in and out of containers, they never really grasped its full meaning. Therefore, they identified it with spirit, much as we identify spirit with alcohol and a variety of abstractions and airy with immaterial, vague, and ethereal. The word pneuma served as a useful symbol whenever concrete descriptions were impossible or unavailable.

The difference in structure between veins and arteries had been fully recognized for about four centuries. Consequently, the two large vessels joining the heart and the lungs caused great difficulties. What we call the pulmonary artery, which in the view of the times should be a vein, since it comes from the liver and thus carries nutrients to the tissues, is actually constructed like an artery, possessing thick walls and apparently showing a pulse. The pulmonary vein, on the other hand, which should be an artery by virtue of its con-

---

[*] L. G. Wilson, "Erasistratus, Galen and the 'Pneuma,'" *Bull. Hist. Med.*, **33**, 298 (1959).

nection with the left ventricle, yet is constructed like a vein and shows no pulse. Galen compromises by calling the former arterial vein and the latter venous artery. These designations are fortified by his descriptions of the structures of veins and arteries. Note that although Galen's observations were made without the benefit of a microscope or even a simple lens, he is fully cognizant that heart muscle differs from voluntary muscle in having nonuniform fibers. Hence he reasons that the heart's function must differ from that of muscle, because he is a firm adherent of the idea that differences in structure correspond to differences in function, a thesis he seeks to prove in many ways. He is thus led to expound the functional distinction between voluntary and cardiac muscle.

The discovery of the difference between sensory and motor nerves, which Galen takes for granted, is historically attributed to Erasistratus (ca. 300 B.C.) just as the discovery of the difference between veins and arteries is attributed to Herophilus (also ca. 300 B.C.); both were great teachers at the school of Alexandria. Galen thus reasons within a sphere of thought already far from a wilderness. But original with Galen is the observation, among many others, that the heartbeat does not stem from motor stimulation since the severance of nerves going to the heart fails to halt its contraction. The heart beats by virtue of its own nature, even if "removed from the thorax." Elsewhere in this work, Galen shows that independent cutting of nerves causes paralysis in specific muscles and limbs. He also points out in Book VIII of *On Anatomical Procedures* that, upon the cutting of appropriate nerves, "the whole natural power of expiration and of utterance is lost," as is demonstrated "in all the experiments causing paralysis, which are four: one by excision of the ribs, another by severing the spinal marrow, a third by severing the nerves, and a fourth by severing the fibres."

That the auricles were not really considered as vital parts of the heart adumbrates the modern trend to call each auricle an atrium. Galen's argument with Aristotle deserves special notice particularly by those who believe that Aristotle's authority kept all minds in a steel vise. Galen does forgive him his mistakes on the ground of his "lacking anatomical experience," adding, however, as if parenthetically, "among his many anatomical errors." But then even dedicated experts like Marinus "have made many mistakes." In other words, anatomy already had its experts and amateurs. Moreover, the science is difficult, and Galen says, "I call all gods to witness that I have often . . . seen things I had completely missed before."

We are offered here, with the illustration of the man "sacrificing a cock to the gods," a glimpse into the nature of superstition. Any anatomical irregularity was regarded as a portent and apparently produced a strong emotional impact. The incident also demonstrates to what extent knowledge can destroy both the fear and the omen.

Exposing the beating heart in a vivisectioned animal is no easy matter, and Galen is confident of his performance. He carefully notes the movements of a dying heart, the quality of ventricular contraction, and the sequence of the heart's contractile waves. He then proceeds to his famous proof that the arteries are not empty of blood. One is rather impressed with the popularity of anatomy in those days and the fact that anatomical demonstrations were public spectacles with large crowds attending and sufficiently interested to lay "down at once a thousand drachmae." Moreover, the "ardent youths" knew when a pseudo-anatomist made a fool of himself. The preparations demanded by the "pompous septuagenarian" bespeak the high operative skill available in the cultural pool of common knowledge.

In describing his famous experiment of inserting a tube into the femoral artery of a dog, Galen states as a matter of course that "obviously there will be no haemorrhage from the severed artery since the upper part, whence comes the blood, is stopped by the ligature." Can anyone doubt that he acts on the assumption that blood flows in the arteries from the heart toward the periphery? Signs of this conception abound throughout his work. However, when he discusses venesection, he remarks, "When you bind the arm, the place round the artery swells into a sizable lump," as if he did not realize that blood from the artery caused the swelling. The fact is that Galen had no specific, consciously formulated theory of the nature of the flow of the blood, for which reason most of his comments bearing upon this issue appear loose, inchoate, or contradictory. In actual situations, whether in discussion or performance, he takes the sound empirical position and states the particular case as accurately as possible.

That Galen should have missed the pulse in the distal segment of the divided artery is indeed surprising, since anyone can see it even if the inserted tube is three inches long. His failure could only be due to his desire to prove, as he explains in his *Whether Blood is Contained in the Arteries in Nature,* that the pulsation of the arteries, although coming from the heart, does not derive from the effect of the heartbeat on materials within the arteries but from some stimulation flowing from the heart along the arterial coats. The first to repeat his experiment was William Harvey in his Second Letter to Jean Riolan. Too bad that Galen was as usual argumentative and self-righteous and accused poor Erasistratus of making "rash assertions without observing." However, Galen was caught thus in the wrong only on rare occasions. Fortunately his utter confusion on the nature of the circulation was unaffected by this error. All he is seeking to show is that arteries are not carriers of air or pneuma but contain blood, and this he establishes beyond a doubt. In his scheme the pulse serves to distribute pneuma and innate heat from the heart throughout the body; thus when an artery is tied off, a limb gets cold. He is the first naturalist to compare the heat of a flame and the innate heat of an animal. The analogy is sheer insight, for his details are weak and he does nothing more with the idea. Yet it no doubt influenced later scientists.

In the second excerpt Galen is concerned with function rather than structure, and he is as brilliant at physiology as he is at anatomy. *On the Functions of Parts of the Human Body* is one of Galen's longest works, first made fully available to the West in 1322, when it was translated from Greek into Latin. It exerted a strong influence until rendered obsolete by modern developments. Note the very foundations of his reasoning in the opening paragraphs. Breathing serves to cool and "refresh" the heart and to remove its soot or exhaust. It fulfills the first function in diastole and the second in systole of the lungs, with the voice as an important by-product. Next there appears a basic assumption that pervades all of Galen's thought—that nature does nothing in vain, that all parts and activities of an organism have a definite purpose within the over-all scheme of the organism's existence; else nature would not have created them in the first place and placed them where they are. This principle that nature does nothing in vain is generally dismissed nowadays as teleological, or purpose-oriented, mysticism.

Even as scholarly a historian as George Sarton says, in *Galen of Pergamon,** that this text of Galen's "was very popular and that is sad, because the influence which it exerted was not by any means good." Sarton marvels: "How could a man as intelligent as Galen fall into such a trap? It was Galen's gratuitous postulation of special forces for each need, even more than his teleology, which risked stopping, and did stop, scientific investigations. . . . To call him a modern, as Singer did, is highly misleading. . . . Far from being modern and progressive, Galen was reactionary in many ways. . . . If we may use present terminology, he was a vitalist opposing the materialists. He was also anti-evolutionist. . . . Being deeply religious, he was more and more tempted to praise the Creator for the infinite marvels of creation. His first principle was Aristotle's: Nature never makes anything which is superfluous; on the strength of it, he tried to justify the form and function of each organ, the perfect adaptation of the former to the latter. . . . Things do not become what they are because they gradually adapt themselves to the rest, but because they have been preadapted from eternity; they are not pushed from behind and below, but dragged from ahead and above." We shall see that this evaluation is mostly hindsight and historically unfair.

The fact is that existing biological structures imply some order at work, since they are the outcome of millenia of natural selection involving cleverly beneficial random mutations. All living forms must therefore be adapted to the niches in which they are found. The concept of adaptation is as characteristic of biology as force is of physics or the covalent bond is of organic chemistry. And what is the vague term "purpose" in biology but "adaptation," or "the function of a part within the context of the organism as a whole"?

There is another feature to the teleological approach. Suppose an anatomist performs a dissection and comes across a swelling, a gland, or some uniqueness in color or texture that catches his eye. He may well be tempted to dismiss the find as unimportant, calling it a growth, a temporary swelling, or what not, and often correctly, because such irregularities do occur. But suppose this anatomist is

---

* Univ. of Kansas Press, Lawrence, Kansas, 1954, pp. 46–58.

a teleologist like Galen. He would then pursue his observation further, as Galen would. Galen reports in his *On the Natural Faculties,* "Instead of admiring nature's skill—they refuse to learn; they even go so far as to scoff, and maintain that the kidneys as well as many other things, have been made by Nature *for no purpose.*" Galen's principle, that everything must have a purpose and that nature does nothing in vain, prevents him from dismissing any element that defies understanding. This kind of outlook is empirically productive. It is also sensible, for the simple reason that traits possessed by an organism must have some selective advantage to have been included in the organism's constitution. If they possessed no advantage, selection would not, as a rule, retain them.

This view can also be overworked, as evidenced by the fact that Galen frequently pays heavily for his attitude. In his avidity to discover the functions, necessarily advantageous, of organs and parts, he falls into concocting Pollyannalike explanations, or rationalizations, to the detriment of scientific rigor. No sooner does he note a phenomenon than he elaborates a justification for its being as is, rather than analyzing, examining, and studying the situation. Nevertheless, the over-all employment of teleology is not as wicked as many critics claim. After all, arteries do lie more deeply than veins, the skull and the cochlea do have exceptionally thick bone, the sella turcica is rather unusually placed—all of which facts are still best interpreted functionally, hence teleologically more or less, as Galen would interpret them. The main issue seems to be the manner of expression.

Galen's reasoning rests organically upon an all-embracing belief-web, which is as fundamental to the mind as air is to a lung-breathing animal or water to a gill-breathing one. Elsewhere in *On the Functions of Parts of the Human Body,* in discussing the Organs of Alimentation, he explains that ingested food gets its primary coction, or digestion, in the stomach. From there it is conveyed to the liver, where it receives refined treatment and final perfection, to become pure blood. The liver then sends forth the blood into the body by means of the veins, all of which, with a few overlooked exceptions, emerge from it and branch out into all the tissues. Crude blood flows to the liver from the viscera through the portal vein, which, being a vein, must also feed the viscera. This dual function creates a complication with which Galen wrestles in the third excerpt. The portal vein fans out in the tissue of the liver, where its branches vanish, while new vessels in the dorsal part of the liver give rise to the hepatic veins and the vena cava. The liver with its vena cava, split into ascending and descending branches, stands in relation to the supply of venous or alimentary blood as the left ventricle with the aorta and its branches stands in relation to the supply of pneuma, or aerated blood. In the refining process in the liver, some exhaust materials are forced into the gall bladder, and others into the spleen. In this scheme the pulmonary artery is part of the venous system. The auricles are mere enlargements, the right ventricle is a venous way station, and the left ventricle is the very hub of the heart. But since nature demonstrated some irregularity in giving the pulmonary artery the walls of an artery and the pulmonary vein the walls of a vein, Galen employs the heaviest artillery in his arsenal of rationalizations to dispose of, or force into harmony, the seemingly discordant facts.

Here is how he expounds the function of the liver in *On the Functions of Parts of the Human Body,* Books IV and XIII.

"It is not for the purpose of elimination that nature has created within the liver an enormous plexus of veins, but for the total sanguination of the nutriment. Had she fashioned in the liver, as in the heart, a large cavity simply to serve as receptacle, and had she further introduced the blood therein through a single vein and led it out through another, the fluid conveyed from the stomach would not tarry one instant in the liver, but rapidly traversing this organ, would be carried along by the force of the stream to be distributed throughout the body." Note that Galen here takes for granted the flow of blood through the heart.

Galen labors under other assumptions. The heart needs the lungs for coolness and for pneuma and operates with an ebb and flow rhythm as do the lungs. It is also the source of "the innate heat that vitalizes the animal" through the two openings of the left ventricle, one leading to the lungs and the other to the arteries. The right ventricle has orifices, too, one of which "brings blood to the heart while the other conducts it to the lung." The blood is here again assumed to be in a state of flow, though its circuit is never defined, apparently because Galen simply never thought of tracing it. Presumably his web of ideas was sufficient for him, comprising a valid, coherent, and gratifying thought pattern within which his mind functioned to its fullest glory and satisfaction.

How could the two streams, the venous and arterial, be one? He would have raged at the mere suggestion of such a circulation. "As we have clearly demonstrated, each organ draws its nurture from neighboring vessels; that deriving from the arteries is quite naturally very fine, while that furnished by the veins is heavy. Arteries have thicker walls than veins, and the blood contained in them is more subtle, more vaporous. Such blood is more suitable to feed soft organs just as thicker blood is more appropriate for denser tissue. . . . The lung is nourished by a perfectly pure blood, yellow-reddish, subtle and charged with air. Blood delivered to it by the heart has all these virtues." Of course, from our vantage point, his scheme is full of contradictions. This situation emphasizes that thought patterns are as immiscible, or uncommunicable, as are strange languages. To Galen, it was clear that venous blood was made by the liver and flowed thence to convey nutriment to all parts of the body; arterial blood was purged in the lungs and warmed in the left ventricle and was also sent to all the tissues of the body. To hint that they merged into one circulating system would be sheer madness, tantamount to saying that blood becomes milk just by flowing into the vessels of the mammary glands, or that ocean water becomes sweet just by flowing into a river bed. Galen devotes an entire volume, *On the Natural Faculties,* to the view that such changes can be brought about only by specialized organs, built by nature for the task. He stresses anastomoses again and again but indicates that their sole purpose is to exchange the substances that the two systems have to offer.

The pulmonary artery and the pulmonary vein constituted quite a problem. According to Galen's scheme, the artery should have been a vein, and the vein an artery. What does a thinker do when confronted with such a situation? The text provides an answer that differs from the one generally given. The usual answer is that when he encounters facts that do not fit the ruling theory, he re-examines, modifies, or replaces that theory. Galen, on the contrary, labors to retain the theory and explain away the exceptions by harmonizing them with his old belief-web.

Is this an unsound procedure, a scientific misdeed? Hardly. We too are often obliged to act in this manner. We did not throw out the gas laws when deviations were found, nor the Periodic Table when some elements failed to fit into their proper places, nor Mendel's laws when linkage or sex-linkage was discovered, nor the wave theory when photons appeared. In some instances harmonizing discordant data through the introduction of correction factors or through clever interpretation is necessary and constructive, whereas in others it seems pathetic or downright silly to later generations. Galen's efforts in this particular instance fall into the latter category. We might say that he thinks he is reasoning but actually he is only rationalizing. The result of his long expatiation and lucubration was that he only achieved peace of mind. In historical perspective, he added nothing to the storehouse of knowledge but merely helped to perpetuate inconsistent and invalid assumptions. His teleology helped him to deceive himself and made it impossible for him to free himself from the chains of theoretical bondage.

Consider next the valves. The arterylike vein (pulmonary artery), which is a "nutritive channel," must not dilate and constrict with the movements of the chest, and there must be in it no backflow of blood. Hence the appropriate structure of the tricuspid valve, which nature opens and closes "at the right moments." Arteries and veins exchange their unique substances through "extremely fine, invisible orifices." The valves promote the exchange by preventing backflow and thus forcing blood nutriment and blood pneuma through the vascular walls. Their membranous flaps are "thrown against the walls of the vein" by the blood's flow in the right direction, at the right time. At diastole "the heart attracts toward itself the fluid . . . which it draws in and traps by means of the membranes." Dilation of the heart, as of a bellows, causes an inward pull. Note that systole is barely mentioned. The dilating movement requires more strength than contraction. Only the weak mitral valve permits some backflow of blood, whereby exhaust material leaves the heart for the lungs.

Finally there is the matter of anastomosis. Galen states that the two blood systems "exchange air and blood through extremely fine, invisible orifices." When the chest contracts at expiration, the tricuspid valve is closed, and the thin-walled pulmonary veins are compressed, so that pneuma flows out of them through tiny pores while venous blood, or rather its nutriment, flows into them, also through tiny pores. This is about all Galen has to say on the subject. In a work not cited here, he does argue with Erasistratus that since in some illnesses, such as pleurisy and pneumonia, anastomoses are destroyed, they must have a purpose, that is, a function, in normal health. On that occasion he describes anastomoses as here. His notions are necessary consequences of his initial assumptions regarding the roles of the venous and arterial blood supplies in the physiology of the whole organism.

It is in connection with anastomoses that we encounter the reference to pores in the interventricular septum. Note that Galen frequently speaks of the veins as if they "worked over" the blood, just as he says that the arteries, "destined to ceaseless motion, require a certain strength and a particular kind of wall" and that, in the veins, "if it [the wall] were thick, many parts of the body would not receive their proper nourishment." He gives two reasons for the existence of the pores in the septum, naturally in terms of his teleological view of organs and their functions. First, the septal pores are part of the general "device of having the veins communicate with the arteries through tiny pores." Second, since the entering vena cava is larger than the emerging pulmonary artery and, correspondingly, the pulmonary vein carrying aerated blood from the lung to the heart is smaller than the emerging aorta, the aorta "carries away part of the blood from the right ventricle." The many claims that Galen postulated a circulatory system with a passage through the septum are obviously false. This passage is wholly incidental and irrelevant to blood flow, and its absence would change no part of Galen's belief-web concerning the venous and arterial blood in the body. The truth is that Galen accepted the blood's flow in veins and arteries but was not prodded by facts or ideas to look for a circulation.

Galen attempts in the third excerpt to resolve a most cumbersome issue. We know that all veins originate from the liver to feed all tissues. But it is also a fact that the portal vein brings blood partly prepared in the stomach from that organ to the liver for final purification. The question then arises, "How are the stomach and viscera nourished?" His answer that venous blood ebbs and flows in the portal vein relies upon analogy, which by and large is one of the mind's main pathways to innovation. That reasoning by analogy sometimes fails does not destroy its value at all, because any scientific investigator knows that nature is opportunistic and always ready to spring new tricks and surprises. It is always ready to lie still and hear out the most specious logic, agree with its unimpeachable syllogistic purity, and then suddenly strike out with whimsical or bewildering novelty.

There is no doubt in Galen's mind that arterial blood acts on a flux and reflux basis, since these vessels "dilate and contract alternately" by virtue of "a power which derives from the heart." He next asserts that arteries "draw in the outer air when they dilate" at the body's periphery and some thin material from the veins at their innermost anastomoses. Those arteries that lie near the heart draw in refined matter "from the heart itself." From the crude intestines and stomach the arteries get nothing. To prove anastomoses between arteries and veins, he cites a beautiful observation: Veins become empty after one or more arteries are cut, thus bringing about fatal bleeding in an animal. No other conclusion is in fact possible from this experiment, unless one functions within a completely different set of ideas, hence within a different belief-web.

Here is how Galen summarizes in his *On the Functions of Parts of the Human Body,* Books VII and IX, his conception of the relation of the heart and lungs to the blood of arteries and veins.

"After having demonstrated that the major role of respiration is the maintenance of natural heat, which is the reason why animals die the moment they are deprived of refrigeration; after having said that its secondary role is to feed the animal spirit, it is fitting to admire nature's work in suiting the lung to these its functions and voice production.

"In confining all the smooth arteries to one center, the heart's left ventricle which houses the principle of natural heat, and in supplying the heart as well with a perpetual means of refrigeration, she deserves our praises. That the heart in contracting diverts all its sooty and fuliginous particles into these same arteries and particularly through the aorta into the others, and that nature took care not to permit the heat of the heart to be extinguished through choking in its pernicious residues, let us sing her praises. That, by creating the lung's soft, porous, and subtle tissue, into which outside air can easily penetrate, she has rendered possible the formation of an aliment fit for animal pneuma, she deserves our admiration. That the lung, composed of three vessels, one vein [the pulmonary artery] and two arteries [the pulmonary vein and trachea], has, nonetheless set aside the trachea to draw in air and expel it in speaking so that we can talk without frequent inhalations, each of which suffices for a long interval, she is indeed worthy of our praises for having chosen the fittest expedient.

· · · · ·

"The lung fills the entire cavity of the thorax in dilating and contracting, as I have explained elsewhere. You have learned there that in all the organs that suck in by first emptying, light substances rush in more rapidly than heavy ones, and large orifices serve to fill the space more rapidly than small ones. You also know that the trachea and bronchi have an orifice at the pharynx and another for the smooth arteries [pulmonary veins] opening into the left ventricle, just as the vein opens into the right ventricle, that the air is inhaled through the pharynx into the bronchi, and that blood is drawn in from the right ventricle through the veins [pulmonary arteries], and a mixture of air and blood from the left ventricle. If you assemble all these facts, you will readily find the proof of what concerns us. In effect, as the lung is expanding, the lightest substance, that is, the outside air, rushes in first and fills the bronchi; next, the mixture from the heart's left ventricle fills the smooth arteries [pulmonary veins]. Finally, the blood arrives [from the right ventricle]. Before the bronchi fill completely with air, nothing can arrive from the other vessels.

· · · · ·

"If you take a dead animal and blow in air through its larynx, you will fill its bronchi and watch its lung attain the greatest distention, while its smooth arteries [pulmonary veins] and veins [pulmonary arteries] retain constant volumes. This proves that nature has made the bronchi capable of obliging the lung to maximum distention, thus forcing the outer air to penetrate the bronchi.

"How is the air drawn into the heart? This takes place when the organ is in diastole, just as the air is expelled in systole. It is essential that the smooth arteries [pulmonary veins] obey the movements of the heart, and the trachea those of the lung. We have already shown that these movements possess two different principles; those of the heart are spontaneous, and those of the thorax are voluntary. We have demonstrated that it was best for respiration to depend upon us and obey the organism's wishes. It seems obvious that the roles of the heart and lung reveal the Creator's foresight and simultaneously skill of the highest degree."

Thus does all fit well together, and Galen's scheme is complete. His scheme, or model, has in fact been prepared after much thought and rejection of unsuitable hypotheses. Its inner harmony is inevitable. That a brilliant anatomist and physiologist of Galen's stature should be excited by the numerous biological adaptations he uncovered is only natural. Only people blinded by a narrow faith in some mechanistic deity can force themselves to remain unimpressed by the biological marvels of function and adaptation. Galen's sense of awe and joy of discovery are understandable. It is also a fact that he sacrificed accuracy in his drive to leave no puzzle unsolved and no challenge unmet and to coerce every incongruity into his cherished pattern. Such conduct is a likely characteristic of such men everywhere and at all times, including our own enlightened age.

It is surely not wrong to conclude that Galen has been far more sinned against than sinning. He has been greatly misrepresented by historians of science and medicine, by men as sincerely dedicated to their tasks as he was to his. Great scholars like Fielding H. Garrison and Arturo Castiglioni speak of him as "this man, to whose authority we owe a perpetuation of fundamental errors which produced a long arrest in medical evolution." Even Charles Singer, who was accused by George Sarton of regarding Galen as a modern, resents Galen's dogmatism, theism, determinism, and neo-Stoicism and says, in *A Short History of Anatomy and Physiology*,* "Galen repeatedly adopts the argument from design for the existence of God; indeed, it is his sole argument." His doctrine was such, Singer

---

* Dover, New York, 1957, pp. 51–2.

continues, that "it was inevitable that it should turn men away from the observation of Nature and that it should make them content with arbitrary solutions of the many problems which his principles raised." Certainly to this statement one might reply, "No more so than the doctrines of Dalton, Darwin, Freud, Harvey, or Claude Bernard." Singer's account of Galen's conception of the vascular system is in fact more of a judgment than a description. A more recent critic of Galen has expressed himself in a similar vein. He comments* "In the last resort, the relation between form (what is anatomically observed) and function (which is attributed by physiological theory) was not for Galen empirical but teleological. It was not established inductively, but *a priori*. The body is a designed creation in which Nature reveals perfect foresight and perfect workmanship; every part in it is ideally suited to its purpose, and functions perfectly. If empirical reasoning with regard to the function of a particular organ fits this absolute and overriding position, then such reasoning may be used; if it does not, then a special theoretical argument must be employed to overcome the apparent discrepancy."

A few words are in order here not so much in Galen's defense as in support of a different approach to the study of the pioneering minds of the past. Let the new approach be termed analytical, and let its pursuers refrain from rendering verdicts and simply seek to determine how brilliant minds operate. Far too little is yet known of the psychological aspects of thought that could lead a keen observer like Galen to explain away the discrepancy in the pulmonary vessels. One cannot charge a man of his caliber with not knowing deduction from induction or fact from fiction, distinctions which any schoolboy can learn. Clearly far deeper forces were involved. Those who measure such geniuses with ordinary yardsticks fail to comprehend the influence of varying sets of assumptions, aims, and values interacting with unique personalities and circumstances. Persistent and dedicated investigation will always yield a theory; acceptance of a theory will always provoke an argument; and defense of a theory will always result in justifying or fitting in exceptions. In numerous instances each of these processes has resulted in great strides forward and vast

* A. R. Hall, "Studies on the History of the Cardiovascular System," *Bull. Hist. Med.*, **34,** 393 (1960).

knowledge, and in a few cases each has ended in frustration or retreat, with the search beginning again in a new direction.

Thus the reader must decide for himself whether Galen is really guilty as charged by his many detractors. All we can say on the basis of the present evidence is that Galen missed the key idea of the blood's circulation. He offered no unified, consistent plan for its flow and never sought one. He knew that blood was in motion, and he knew the direction of motion in the region of the heart. But he felt quite content to leave the matter there, presumably because he did not see anything inadequate or unsound about his own scheme. He saw few contradictions in it, and those he discerned he easily fitted into the framework of basic assumptions he considered unchallengeable. He was probably aware that there were things he did not perceive, but such is the state of science at any time.

4. IBN NAFIS

[*Abu-l-Hasan Ala-ud-Din Ali ibn Abi-l-Hazm*]

A Thirteenth-Century Manuscript on Blood

Our purpose now is to set forth what we
have been able to find of the discussions of
the Sheikh, the Rais, Abi Ali al-Husein
Ibn Abdallah Ibn Sina, on anatomy in his
Canon, and that by collecting what he
wrote in the first book of the Canon and
the third book of the same, and so arrange
properly all that he wrote on anatomy.
What has deterred us from engaging in
dissection is the authority of the law and
our inherent compassion. So we see fit to
depend, for the description of the internal
organs, on the words of those who have
preceded us—of those engaging in dissection—especially the honorable Galen, as
his books are the best books that have
come down to us on this subject. . . . We
have relied chiefly . . . on his sayings, except in a few details which we thought
might be mistakes of copyists or the fact
that his description had not been given
after a thorough observation. In describing the use of these organs we have depended on true observation and honest
study, regardless of whether or not these
fit the theories of those who have preceded
us. . . . We see fit, before starting the dis-

From S. I. Haddad and A. A. Khairallah, "A Forgotten Chapter in the History of the Circulation of
the Blood," *Annals of Surgery*, **104,** 1 (1936).

cussion of anatomy, to write a preface that will help us to understand this science. The preface contains five discussions. The first is on the difference that animals show regarding their organs.

And we say, and God is the All-Knowing, whereas, one of the functions of the heart is the creation of the spirit from very thin blood strongly miscible with air, and air, so it is necessary to make, in the heart, very thin blood to make possible the creation of the spirit from that mixture. The place where the spirit is created is in the left cavity of the two cavities of the heart. Therefore, it is necessary, in the heart of man and his like—of those who have lungs—to have another cavity where the blood is thinned to become fit for mixing with the air. For if the air is mixed with the blood while it is still thick, it would not make a homogeneous mixture. This cavity (where the blood is thinned) is the right cavity of the two cavities of the heart. If the blood is thinned in this cavity it must of necessity pass to the left cavity where the spirit is created. *But between these two cavities there is no passage as that part of the heart is closed and has no apparent openings as some believed and no non-apparent opening fit for the passage of this blood as Galen believed.* The pores of the heart there are obliterated and its body is thick, and there is no doubt that the blood, when thinned, *passes in the vena arteriosa to the lung to permeate its substance and mingle with the air, its thinned part purified; and then passes in the arteria venosa to reach the left cavity of the two cavities of the heart; having mixed with the air and* become fit for the creation of the spirit. What is left of this mixture, less attenuated, the lung uses for its own nourishment. This is the reason why the vena arteriosa is made of thick walls and of two coats, so that what passes through its pores be very thin, and the arteria venosa thin and of one coat.

. . . . .

The lung is composed of parts one of which is the bronchi, the second the branches of the arteria venosa and the third the branches of the vena arteriosa, and all of these are connected by loose porous flesh. . . . *The need of the lung for the vena arteriosa* is to transport to it the blood that has been thinned and warmed in the heart, so that what seeps through the pores of the branches of this vessel into the alveoli of the lung may mix with what there is of air therein and combine with it, the resultant composite becoming fit to be spirit when this mixing takes place in the left cavity of the heart. The mixture is carried to the left cavity by the *arteria venosa*. What is left of that blood in the inside of the branches of the vena arteriosa and passes through its apertures to the body of the lung, would be thicker than the blood that seeps through and more watery, and fit for the nourishment of the lung. This vena arteriosa while it brings to the lung its nourishment, also brings the blood that is very thin and that is fit to become animal spirit when mixed with the air. The use of arteria venosa is to transmit this air that is mixed with the thinned blood to the left cavity of the two cavities of the heart to become spirit. Another use is for the passage of what is left in this cavity of that mixture which was not fit for the creation of the spirit and of what is left in it of air that is overheated and useless. Both of these must come out of the cavity to make space for what comes afterwards of air alone or of air mixed with greatly thinned blood. So this vessel carries back these things to the lung to be discharged with the returning breath (expiration).

. . . . .

The function of the heart, as we have shown, is first, the creation of animal spirit and its distribution to the organs in order to animate them. This creation comes about by heating the blood and making it thin so that when it is mixed with what there is of air in the lung, the mixture becomes fit for the production of the animal spirit. . . . *Therefore, for the nourishment of the spirit that is in the heart, it is necessary for the blood to become attenuated in the heart and its consistency very much thinned, then pass to the lung and mix with what there is of air there and be cooked in it until it is tempered and become fit for the nourishment of the spirit, and afterwards pass to the spirit that is in the heart and mix with it and nourish it. . . .* So of necessity the heart should have one cavity to contain the blood and thin it and another cavity to contain the spirit, and from this latter cavity the spirit passes to the different organs. And of necessity the cavity which contains the blood should be near the liver where the blood is made and so must be on the right side of the heart as the liver is on the right side of the body; and the cavity which contains the spirit on the left side of the heart. . . . And his (Avicenna's) statement that the heart has three ventricles . . . is not correct as the heart has only two ventricles, one filled with blood on the right side and the other filled with the spirit on the left side, *and between these two there is absolutely no opening for if there were, the blood would pass to the place of the spirit and spoil its essence. Also dissection gives the lie to what they said, as the septum between these two cavities is much thicker than elsewhere, lest some blood or spirit pass through and get lost.* . . . Again, his (Avicenna's) statement that the blood that is in the right side is to nourish the heart is not true at all, for the nourishment to the heart is from the blood that goes through the vessels that permeate the body of the heart. . . . *The benefit of this blood (that is in the right cavity) when it is thinned and attenuated is to go up to the lung, mix with what is in the lung of air, then pass through the arteria venosa to the left cavity of the two cavities of the heart and of that mixture is created the animal spirit.*

The Galenic Foundation

It is fortunate that this *Forgotten Chapter in the History of the Circulation of the Blood* has recently been unearthed, because it demonstrates that Galen's achievements exerted as potent an influence on the Moslem scholars as upon the Christian naturalists who followed them. Moslem physicians delved into Galen's writings with wholehearted and unabated enthusiasm for about five-hundred years, with no sign of a desire to change or abandon his approach and outlook. On the contrary, the period brought forth many telling commentaries on Galen and many paeons of praise for him. By the thirteenth century, the time of Ibn Nafis, Christian scholars were already acquainted with Galen, and they remained under his sway for another three-hundred years. Such power must be deserved and springs mainly from the intrinsic merit of Galen's physiological and anatomical accounts, as well as from his stimulating speculations.

The author of the segment presented here is known to have studied medicine in Damascus and to have practiced it at the Mansoury Hospital in Cairo, Egypt, which he later headed as dean. He enjoyed a great reputation as a physician and left behind him several highly honored medical works. Like many of the great scholars of both ancient Greece and the Moslem world, he was learned in philosophy, religion, and literature and composed numerous books on subjects other than medicine. Unlike Galen or Aristotle, he was no biological experimentalist, since he refrained from dissection by "authority of the law and our inherent compassion." Whatever he has to say is therefore the product of critical analyses of Galen's facts and logical considerations. His claim that he "depended on true observation and honest study" can only be taken to reflect his high opinion of Galen's research and records, since these seem to be the only sources he relies upon.

The heart, says Ibn Nafis, creates spirit from thin blood. Ordinary blood finds its way to the right ventricle, where the thinning takes place and whence it cannot pass directly to the left ventricle because the thick interventricular septum "has no apparent opening . . . fit for the passage of this blood as Galen believed." But the thinned blood must get to the left ventricle, where some activity or coction occurs to produce animal spirit within the red fluid, which, thus modified, is distributed "to the organs in order to animate them." The septum cannot have pores; leakage of blood as yet untreated by the air of the lungs from the right ventricle into the left one would interfere with the latter's task of manufacturing animal spirit.

The thinned blood flows from the right ventricle, where incidentally it is also warmed, to the lungs via the pulmonary artery, which was then referred to as the arterylike vein ("arterylike" because of its thick walls). It apparently carries two kinds of blood, a thin, refined component and a thicker, heavier residue. Although Ibn Nafis denies any flow across the septum because it has no "apparent pores," he is quite willing to bestow pores upon the pulmonary artery, where certainly none can be seen. The septum does in fact possess deceptive pits, but the walls of the pulmonary artery show no indications of openings whatever. Yet he declares that thinned and warmed blood "seeps through the pores," mixes with air in the lung alveoli, and proceeds through the pulmonary vein (the veinlike artery) to the left ventricle for the next step, which is its endowment with animal spirit. The walls of the arterylike vein are thicker than those of normal veins so as to conserve the thick blood for delivery to the lungs as nutriment. It is this thick residue, presumably the bulk of the venous blood, that "passes through its apertures to the body of the lung" in order to feed that organ. The thin blood mixes with the air in the lung alveoli, to "become fit for the creation of the spirit." It is this fraction that is collected by the pulmonary vein (the veinlike artery) and conveyed to the left ventricle. But the pulmonary vein has other functions as well. It "carries back . . . to the lung" "air that is overheated and useless," left over from the spirit-making reaction in the left ventricle, and blood from the right ventricle that was found "not fit for the creation of the spirit" in the left ventricle.

Let us examine what this outstanding scholar and physician is doing here. To begin with, he is building upon Galen's foundation of facts and assumptions. He states that blood is made by the liver and that for this reason the right ventricle, the first way station in the blood's elaboration, is situated near the liver. When the thickness of the arterylike vein confronts him, he finds an excellent reason for it, too, even as Galen did. Galen knew that blood flowed from the right ventricle to the lungs, that air was essential to life, and that blood flowed from the lungs to the left ventricle and from the left ventricle to the entire body. And yet, although aware of all these facts, Galen did not develop them. Since they had no particular prominence in his scheme, he left them a blur in his voluminous writings. With Ibn Nafis a new element definitely is introduced. This new element is not a new fact or a new scheme; it is merely a new significance engendered by a slightly different way of looking at the old scheme, from a slightly different angle, so that different facets catch the light and reflect it with a strong beam.

This shift of emphasis was not apparent to the Moslem students of anatomy and physiology. At any rate, they put it to no practical use. However, some two-hundred years later, another scholar, with no knowledge of Ibn Nafis' work, called attention to the same aspect of the blood's flow, the pulmonary circulation. This man, as we shall see, was Michael Servetus.

5. ANDREAS VESALIUS

The Epitome

Of the organs which are created for re-kindling the natural heat within us and for the restoration and nourishment of our spirits, the heart is considered by far the most important part of the agitative faculty. It is like a pine nut, compressed in front and behind, located with its base under the middle of the breastbone and its apex inclining sharply forward to the left side. The substance of the heart is fleshy, but like the substance of muscles, and is interwoven with a tougher threefold type of fibers provided with its own veins and arteries.

The heart has two sinuses or ventricles. One is located on the right side; this is broader and appears to be covered with a thinner and looser substance of the heart. The orifice of the vena cava extends to this ventricle and is furnished with three membranes drawn inward. Likewise, a vessel which is like an artery in form but performs the function of a vein and hence is called the arterial vein proceeds from this ventricle; this vessel sends toward the orifice of the ventricle also three small

From *The Epitome,* translated by L. R. Lind, Macmillan, New York, 1949, Chapter IV (Concerning the Heart and the Organs Which Minister to Its Functions), pp. 57–61.

67

membranes facing outward. The other ventricle, surrounded by a special thick substance of the heart, lies on the left side. It, too, has two orifices, of which the lower, with two membranes closing inward, belongs to a certain vessel, an artery. While it is formed like a vein, this vessel holds the air and performs the function of an artery; hence it is called the venous artery; this artery sends two membranes that close inward to its own orifice. The higher orifice is dedicated to the beginning of the great artery, to which Nature has also given three membranes facing outward. These ventricles are separated by a very thick septum adapted for distending and contracting and (like the ventricles of the heart) built up within of many pits of ample size.

The entire heart is covered with a certain membranous involucrum, to which it is joined at no point. This involucrum is much more ample than the heart and is moistened within by an aqueous humor. The lower region of the involucrum is attached on the outside to a transverse septum of no small breadth; on its two sides the involucrum is contained by the membranes interposed in the cavity of the thorax, supporting this involucrum in order that the heart may be supported in position.

The lung fills the rest of the cavity of the thorax not occupied by the heart, the membranes just mentioned, and the descending esophagus. The lung adapts itself on all sides, as the liver does, to the shape of the parts lying close by; on both right and left sides it resembles the hoof of a cow or some other cloven-hoofed animal. Each lung is divided into two fibers or lobes built up from many interweavings of vessels. The rough artery is led down from the top of the throat (where also the tonsils and two other types of glands are located) to the thorax; it is partly cartilaginous so that the voice may be produced. In order that the lung may be expanded and relaxed and thus may assist breathing, it is partly membranous, filled here and there with branches. The arterial vein, proceding from the right ventricle of the heart which prepares the blood familiar to the lung, offers the blood to the lung; it is distributed in an innumerable series to the latter. Similarly, the venous artery intertwines the lung with an abundant series. These vessels are surrounded by the spongy, soft, foamy, and quite pliable substance proper to the lung. A quite small thin tunic lies next to this substance, not hindering the dilatation and compression of the lung in any way; this tunic is always contiguous to the tunic which lines the ribs.

The lung causes a motion of the thorax dependent upon our wills; it dilates to produce a vacuum, and by virtue of this the air from outside ourselves passes along the uvula. When we breathe deeply, the air is attracted through the mouth as though into a bellows. A small part of the air seeks the brain through the foramina of the skull, while the remainder enters the rough artery [trachea] by way of the upper throat and completely fills the cavity of the lung made by the latter's dilatation. The substance of the lung changes this air by force peculiar to itself, adapting the air to the use of the heart. This allows the best part of the air to be taken up by the branches of the venous artery from the offshoots of the rough artery extending throughout so that, by the intervention of the former artery, the air may be carried to the left sinus of the heart, where it is going to perfect the material of the vital spirit.

The heart attracts this air and draws a large supply of blood from the right ventricle into the left ventricle. From the steamy vapor of that blood and from that air, by the inborn virtue of its own substance, the heart creates the spirit which the blood with a rushing flow distributes, thus accompanied and nourished, to the entire body through the great artery; the heart tempers the native heat of each part in the same way that the respiration restores the tinder of the innate heat to the heart. Thus the respiration and the pulse have the same use; by their rhythms the great artery of the heart is dilated and constricted. The heart therefore uses the air for making the vital spirit, and the fiery heat of the heart is tempered by the air. Whatever is sooty and unsuitable for production of the spirit is returned to the lung through the venous artery and, together with the air which had remained

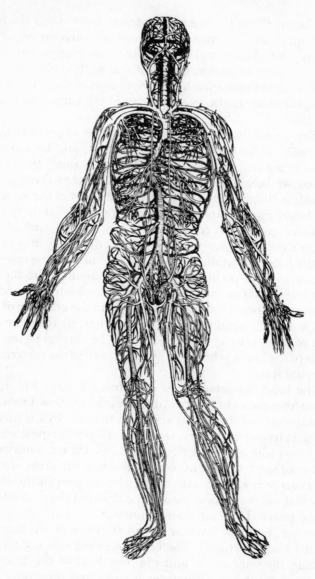

The vena cava and its branches, drawn as a continuous system. The figure shows the influence of traditional notions of structure and many nonhuman features.

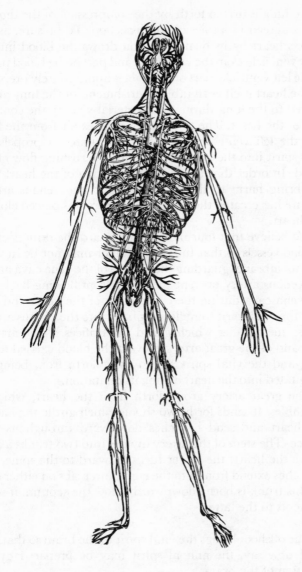

The arterial system. This figure also shows the influence of traditional notions of structure and many nonhuman features.

in the lung is driven forth by the compression of the thorax; this is agreed by professors of dissection. To be sure, as the tireless heart by its own dilatation draws the blood into its right ventricle from the vena cava and part of the blood passes to the left ventricle, part of it in fact is appropriately prepared by the heart itself as suitable nourishment for the lung and is offered to the lung through the arterial vein by the contraction of the heart. The dilated heart takes air from the lung into the left ventricle, but when constricted it propels the vital spirit into the great artery with the rushing flow of the blood. In order that the rapid contraction of the heart may not bring harm to the vena cava and the venous artery, Nature has created the auricles as storerooms placed close to the heart.

We believe that four membranes guard the orifices of the cardiac vessels so that the heart's labor may not be in vain. The membranes guarding the orifices of the vena cava and of the venous artery prevent the blood from flowing back into the vena cava during the contraction of the heart and prevent the vital spirit from flowing back into the venous artery. Those membranes which guard the orifices of the arterial vein and of the great artery prevent the blood carried to the lung and the vital spirit already sent forth from being regurgitated into the heart during its dilatation.

The great artery grows forth from the heart, which it resembles. It sends forth two shoots which girdle the base of the heart and send branches downward through its substance. The stem of the artery divides into two trunks a little above the heart; the larger turns leftward to the spine, and branches extend from it to the eight lower ribs on either side. As this trunk is borne downward below the septum, it sends offshoots to the latter.

. . . . .

The offshoot brings the vital spirit to the brain so that, as I shall now say, the animal spirit may be prepared by the function of the brain.

Vesalius Accepts and Passes On

Vesalius was a master anatomist of rare skill and courage. He was no rebel defying authorities, like his contemporary Paracelsus or Giordano Bruno, who appeared a few decades after him. He was too busy applying his genius to the work that was his calling, and if his findings differed from those of some past master, he voiced his disagreement simply because he had to report what his own eyes had observed. The recognized leaders were not ignoramuses or incompetents or deceivers. They merely failed to see what he had plainly and laboriously unearthed. Some great anatomists just miss a point or two, Galen noted. In the words of Hippocrates, the art is difficult. And Galen was the man whom Vesalius admired above all his teachers and whom he quoted in worshipful respect innumerable times. He did not pursue his studies to depose or belittle Galen but to praise him, although he frequently contradicted him. "As the gods love me," he exclaims, "I, who yield to none in my devotion for Galen, neither can nor should enjoy any greater pleasure than praising him. . . . I hear that many are hostile to me because I have held in contempt the authority of Galen, the prince of physicians and preceptor of all . . . because I have not indiscriminately accepted all his opinions." Vesalius argues with sincerity that Galen would be proud to see him rectify some of his errors and omissions. Thus it was truly a labor of love when in 1541, at the age of twenty-seven, Vesalius aided in the editing of Galen's *Collected Works* for a Venetian publisher.

Three points should be borne in mind in any consideration of Vesalius' era. First, every writer of the period referred to "the ancients," which means that he was conscious of the passage of time and of the possibility of changes in the interim. Second, each writer condemned superstition by name and repeatedly urged the study of nature and respect for experience in place of worship of authority and books. Third, each writer questioned and criticized prevailing views, even those of the most honored masters. When an idea goes unchallenged for generations, it must be so sacrosanct, so central to the life and thought of the culture, so potent in its appeal under the circumstances, that talented minds are incapable of freeing themselves from its grip sufficiently to see it in perspective.

Many historians adopt the nineteenth-century attitude of blaming people and institutions rather than the nature of man for the slow development of human dissection. According to Lind, who translated *The Epitome*, "Anatomy, like astronomy, was a study always a bit suspected among churchmen. The procurement of cadavers was often a perilous business. Galen was the anatomical authority accepted by the Church. Yet Vesalius revolutionized anatomy, dissected cadavers without subterfuge or reticence in his public demonstrations, stole the bodies when necessary, and showed beyond a doubt that Galen knew anatomy only from the dissection of apes, dogs, and pigs—and did not thoroughly understand even the anatomy of these animals. The Church, nevertheless, did not lay hands upon Vesalius. Galileo and Servetus suffered under the Inquisition, but not Vesalius." It is a fact that Galen was held in high esteem by the Church leadership and by all physicians, scientists, and scholars. On the other hand, cadavers had been dissected in classical antiquity by men who dedicated themselves to the art of healing, as witness Galen's admonition in his *On Anatomical Procedures:* "Make it rather your serious endeavor not only to acquire accurate book-knowledge of each bone but also to examine assiduously with your own eyes the human bones themselves. This is quite easy at Alexandria because the physicians there employ ocular demonstrations in teaching osteology to students. For this reason, if for no other, try to visit Alexandria." Galen goes on to recount how he was able to obtain human skeletons. And if a physiologist like Galen studied bones in this manner, it is hard to see how he could suppress the natural desire to investigate other organs as well. Besides, he was for years physician to gladiators. Little wonder that he states further on, "For men have often rapidly observed whatever they wished in bodies of men condemned to death and thrown to wild beasts, or in brigands lying unburied on a hillside. Again, extensive wounds and ulcers, reaching deep down, have exposed many parts which were recognized by the experienced as having the same structure as in the bodies of apes. . . . By frequently dissecting many bodies of exposed children, they were persuaded that man has the same bodily structure as an ape. In the course of various surgical operations that we perform, sometimes removing mortified flesh, sometimes cutting out bones, the likeness becomes apparent to the practised eye. . . . What I have just said as to the veins in the lower arm and hand can all be ascertained in man before dissection in many cases."

As far back as almost two centuries before Galen, Celsus wrote,* "Moreover, as pains, and also various kinds of diseases, arise in the more internal parts, they [i.e. the Rationalists] hold that no one can apply remedies for these who is ignorant about the parts themselves; hence it becomes necessary to lay open the bodies of the dead and to scrutinize their viscera and intestines. They hold that Herophilus and Erasistratus [circa 300 B.C.] did this in the best way by far, when they laid open men whilst alive—criminals received out of prison from the kings—and whilst these were still breathing, observed parts which beforehand nature had concealed. . . . Nor is it, as most people say, cruel that in the execution of criminals, and but a few of them, we should seek remedies for innocent people of all future ages."

Vesalius seems to have managed fairly well with cadavers. According to Fallopius, the majority of Italian physicians supported and admired him. On visiting Bologna, he performed dissections at the request of his host, Professor Andreas Albius and others, two bodies being placed at his disposal. He demonstrated the vascular system, and an acrimonious debate ensued concerning the origin of the blood, indicating that no one was hampered in his beliefs and that the period abounded in argumentation. On that same triumphal tour through Italy, in 1543–4, directly after the publication of his great *On the Fabric of the Human Body* and his brief popularization of it, *The Epitome,* Vesalius went to Pisa at the invitation of Cosimo de Medici, the Duke of Tuscany, who wished to hire him as his permanent physician, in spite of the fact that he was then physician to the emperor. A special theater was constructed in Pisa, so that all who were interested might watch a dissection by Vesalius. So great was the crowd that the scaffolding collapsed. As C. Singer notes in his *A Short History of Anatomy and Physiology,*† "in 1319 during

---

* Celsus, *De Medicina,* Vol. I, translated by W. G. Spencer, Harvard Univ. Press, Cambridge, Mass., 1935, p. 15.

† Dover, New York, 1957, p. 121.

Mondino's lifetime, we hear of students at Bologna being prosecuted for body-snatching." Since dissection was obligatory then at some universities, "the authorities came to wink at the proceedings." The same situation began to prevail elsewhere, and prejudice "eased under the Papacy of Sixtus IV (1471–84) and more so under Clement VII (1523–4). Yet, later Rome itself became something of an anatomical centre, though less important than Padua or Bologna."

Nor did Vesalius revolutionize anatomy by dissecting "cadavers without subterfuge or reticence." Singer says that "dissection had become comparatively common at Bologna by the end of the first quarter of the fourteenth century," that is, a good two centuries before Vesalius. Furthermore, Vesalius never saw himself as a pioneer at dissecting or believed that dissection was a novel practice or that there existed exceptional regulations against it. True, in his Dedicatory Letter to Philip II, in *The Epitome,* he complains, as many medical writers still do, that most physicians were ignorant of the essentials of anatomy. And he adds, "I pass over in silence those pestilent doctors who encompass the destruction of the common life of mankind, who never even stood by at a dissection: whereas in the knowledge of the body no one could produce anything of value who did not perform dissections with his own hands as the kings of Egypt were wont to do and in the like manner busied himself frequently and sedulously with dissections and with simple medicines." Dedicated physicians, however, "as children in the home learn reading and writing, so they exercised the dissection of cadavers and, learned in this wise, under the happy auspices of the Muses, they bent to their studies." He asserts in the same paragraph that "Galen, . . . although easily chief of the masters, nevertheless did not dissect the human body; and the fact is now evident that he described (not to say imposed upon us) the fabric of the ape's body, although the latter differs from the former in many respects." It is, of course, possible that Vesalius' information on Galen's dissecting habits is as reliable as his story about the assiduous anatomical researches of the kings of Egypt.

Among the outstanding anatomists and physicians in the decades before Vesalius were Berengario da Carpi, Andreas de Laguna,

Charles Estienne, Nicolaus Massa, and John Dryander. They opened wombs to inspect fetuses, examined newborn monsters, injected hot water into the kidneys and bladder, operated for bladder stones, looked for Aristotle's third ventricle, studied the structure of muscles and organs and the role of the lungs in breathing and speaking, compared human and ape bodies, and cited clinical experiences in their hospitals. "If we consider the picture of the anatomical searcher of the first half of the sixteenth century . . . , we shall find him critical of tradition, striving to create his own conception through dissections, and increasingly convinced of the rightness of his personal observation and judgment.* Moreover, "there was no battle for the acceptance of the new anatomy and the new method of observation: both were accepted at once."†

Vesalius was never a revolutionary out to demolish past reputations. As a person phenomenally adept at dissection and surgery, he was bound to differ with Galen, the predecessor he revered most, much as his successors were to differ with him. If it is true, as is claimed, that Vesalius corrected approximately 200 errors perpetrated by Galen, it is also true that those who followed Vesalius discovered even a greater number of errors committed by him. It is pertinent to cite here the comment of John F. Fulton:‡ "In 1943 at the time of the four hundredth anniversary of the Fabrica we had a contest among the students to see who could discover the greatest number of errors in the muscle plates. Two students tied for the prize, each having found 21 inaccuracies." At the very height of his career Vesalius was criticized, although with inordinate mildness, in a work called *Observationes Anatomicae,* by Gabriel Fallopius, a self-confessed disciple of "the divine Vesalius." Vesalius accepted the criticism graciously.

---

* G. Rath, "Pre-Vesalian Anatomy in the Light of Modern Research," *Bull. Hist. Med.,* **35,** 148 (1961).
† M. F. Ashley Montagu, in E. A. Underwood, ed., *Science, Medicine, and History,* Vol. I, Oxford Univ. Press, London, 1953, p. 380.
‡ *Vesalius Four Centuries Later,* Univ. of Kansas Press, Lawrence, Kansas, 1950, p. 17.

Anatomists will never be wholly free from social restrictions on the use of human corpses. Disposal of the dead, whether by cremation, burial, or exposure to beasts, has always been an occasion for somber rites. It is wrong to say that priests invented or introduced these rituals. Religion creates few, if any, new customs or institutions but rather sanctions what is already in existence, supplying new explanations or meanings for old practices. Islam, for example, did not originate the veil, the prohibition of pork, circumcision, or the adoration of the Kaaba. Nor did Judaism fully originate the Passover, or Christianity Christmas, since both are refurbished old pagan holidays. No human culture has ever allowed the unlimited dissection of human corpses. The bodies of the dead are regarded with a unique mixture of awe, fear, respect, devotion, duty, and taboo, and to this day people everywhere demand burial for the corpses of those related to them by bonds of blood. Even impersonal modern communities seek to render the customary formalities for those who die within their jurisdictions. It is reported of New York City that "Last year [1960] the bodies of 2000 adults went unclaimed at Bellevue morgue, the busiest of several maintained by the city. A few went to medical colleges, but most of them wound up in an unmarked grave on Hart Island, the city's 'Potter's Field.'" The surfeit of unclaimed corpses notwithstanding, it is still difficult, if not impossible, for a private physician or student of biology to obtain a cadaver to take home and practice anatomy on. Many times the author has asked undergraduate biology students how many would be willing to leave their bodies to the medical school. Generally about five per cent volunteer, but only about one per cent say that they would so treat the bodies of their parents. With older students both fractions are much reduced.

Just as in the Middle Ages many people offered to sell their souls for some immediate gain, so today quite a few individuals offer to sell their bodies to medical schools. Several administrators have reported that such transactions are out of the question. In the first place, a man's corpse belongs to his next of kin, not to himself. Second, a prospective seller is usually shiftless, so even if his kin would agree to honor the sale, the chances are that his death would occur far from home and that no funds would be available for delivery of the body to the buyer.

However strongly human dissection was frowned upon, its prohibition did not everywhere go unchallenged. With the progress of learning in ancient Greece, and later in the Middle Ages in Europe, more and more conflict developed between man's traditional attitude toward the dead and his growing desire to know the fabric of the human body in health and disease. Although some scholars bowed to convention and desisted from anatomizing on the ground that it would displease God and man, others constructed for their consciences excellent rationalizations and proceeded to evolve the science of anatomy. Strict compromises were effected. Some human dissection was permitted to qualified men or institutions, stealthily at first and then quite openly. In the beginning the bodies of criminals only were used, and later the corpses of unclaimed individuals. This arrangement prevails in fact at the present time, and the inner conflict is still with us. In some states of the Union, medical schools still have trouble in obtaining adequate numbers of cadavers, and legislatures and city councils are often confronted with bills calling for an end to dissection and a decent burial for every corpse. As soon as prejudice against dissection relaxed, body snatching and grave robbing became common. To pass their anatomy examinations or pursue an absorbing investigation, some tyros readily resorted to theft. In time there appeared the ugly phenomenon of Burke and Hale, the two medical students who, too impatient to wait for doomed patients to die naturally, helped them along just a bit in order to sell their bodies to eagerly waiting customers, usually fellow students. Since one evil deed leads to another, they eventually finished off fairly healthy persons as well. Obviously the free use of cadavers is beset with grave social dangers.

Galen undoubtedly dissected human bodies. However, probably because in the absence of good preservatives and refrigeration human parts were not always available for teaching or demonstration purposes, in composing his texts he made use of materials from dogs or apes. Apparently Vesalius did the same. This procedure would not be required today, when medical supply houses sell human skeletons and highly naturalistic models. Likely neither Galen nor Vesalius objected to utilizing dogs or apes to illustrate points after he had indicated quite explicitly that he was familiar with human anatomy. A recent evaluation of the great masterpiece of Vesalius substantiates these conclusions.* "Thus, between 1537 and 1542 the whole of his experience of the female generative organs was founded on six bodies. Three had to be used for public demonstrations. Of the others, one was of a six-year-old girl and had been stolen by a student from the grave. It was in a wretched state of preservation, and could hardly be used except for the study of the bones. There thus remained only two for purposes of private study. Of these one was a pregnant woman that had been murdered. Vesalius seems to have been forced to dissect this body very rapidly in the course of a post-mortem examination, conducted for judicial purposes. In accord with this is the inferiority of his description of the pregnant uterus and foetus. The remaining female corpse was of a woman that had been hanged. It is on her that the anatomy of the female generative organs in the Fabrica is substantially based. Small wonder that Vesalius followed Galen in frequently drawing his conclusions from the bodies of animals!

. . . . .

"Vesalius contradicts Galen in denying that man has a separate Pre-maxillary bone and he contrasts him in this respect with the dog. Oddly enough, his figure of the Hyoid bone is probably actually taken from the dog. Vesalius has admirable representations of the vertebrae in the different regions, distinguishing their types, comparing them with those of the ape, and bringing out the salient features in the spinal curves. His figures of the ribs are less satisfactory and contain a considerable number of errors.

. . . . .

"The scapula is not among the best figures of Vesalius. . . . The sternum is better."

Consider now Vesalius' interpretation of the vascular system and the function of the heart and blood. He adheres closely to the beliefs of his time and offers nothing new on the subject. His description of the veins and arteries, the heart, and its valves and chambers is as clear as his keen eye allows, but his underlying assumptions are conventional. The right ventricle "prepares the blood familiar to the lung, offers the blood to the lung. . . . The lung

---

* C. Singer, *A Short History of Anatomy and Physiology,* Dover, New York, 1957, pp. 119, 123.

causes a motion of the thorax dependent upon our wills." The pulmonary vein "holds the air and performs the function of an artery." It conveys the air "to the left sinus of the heart, where it is going to perfect the material of the vital spirit. The heart attracts this air and draws a large supply of blood from the right ventricle into the left ventricle."

Vesalius' genius and his innovations in anatomy were of gigantic proportions, but no traces of them were left in this sector. What is found is a mere reiteration of the seemingly coherent but actually utterly confused traditional notions, with an original one added here and there that serves only to fortify the old belief-web rather than to weaken it. Vesalius accepts the prevailing theories on the functions of the veins and arteries and regards the left ventricle as the seat of formation of "the material of the vital spirit" and the right ventricle as the place where part of the blood from the vena cava "is appropriately prepared" for the special needs of the lungs. It would be inconceivable to him to have other views. On what could they be based, unless one hit upon a totally new scheme?

Note the lack of clarity of the concepts and simultaneously their inclusion of all the known data. The intake of air is accounted for, and hence the role of the lungs, evidently to Vesalius' intellectual satisfaction. Respiration supplies some component of the vital spirit and also restores the heart's heat, which the arteries distribute to all parts of the body. But "the fiery heat of the heart is tempered by the air," and the pulmonary vein, which brings into the heart air "from the offshoots of the rough artery extending throughout" the lung, somehow serves as well to return to the lung the sooty and unsuitable materials accumulating in the heart as by-products of its activities. The inconsistency of this pattern is obvious to us, but the pioneers who formulated it were not bolstered by knowledge of oxygen, hemoglobin, oxygenation, oxygen release, oxidation, diffusion, metabolism, air as a mixture of gases, the pumping action of the heart, arterial pressure, capillary anastomoses, and so on. Consequently, how can we judge them?

Like Galen, Vesalius vaguely presupposes some kind of blood flow, but the scheme is as unformed in his mind as are our contemporary ideas on the nature of memory, the meaning of sensation, the meaning of attraction, the nature of a field of force, the causes of the rise and fall of nations, and the making of a criminal. Future scholars may wonder how we failed to see what seems so clear to them. Yet we continue to rely on our beliefs, unaware of possible inconsistencies. Galen and Vesalius were in the same position. They knew that the blood was in a state of flow, and they knew that it followed specific courses in and out of the heart, but they were unable to conceive of the circulatory mechanism as a whole, as we do, partly because they were satisfied with their own assumptions and explanations.

6. MICHAEL SERVETUS
The Restoration of Christianity

[CHRISTIANISMI RESTITUTIO]

Not only because of such gifts, but by reason of that one alone who breathes the
divine spirit into us, God is said to give us
his spirit, Gen. 2 and 6. Our soul is a kind
of lantern of God, Prov. 20. It is like a
spark of the spirit of God, a reflection of
the wisdom of God, created yet very similar to that spiritual wisdom, incorporated
in it, retaining the innate light of divinity,
the spark of that prime wisdom and the
very spirit of divinity. God himself testifies,
in chapter 6 above, that the spirit of divinity was innate in man even after
Adam's sin. The dispensation of our life
is given and is sustained through grace
from his breath, as Job says, chap. 10 and
32 and following. God breathed the divine
spirit into Adam's nostrils together with
a breath of air, and thence it remains,
Isaiah 2 and Psa. 103. God himself maintains the breath of life for us by his spirit,
giving breath to the people who are upon
the earth and spirit to those treading it, so
that we live, move and exist in him, Isaiah
42 and Acts 17. Wind from the four winds

From C. D. O'Malley, *Michael Servetus. A Translation of His Geographical, Medical and Astrological Writings with Introductions and Notes,* American Philosophical Society, Philadelphia, 1953, pp. 201–8 (The Resto-ration of Christianity).

and breath from the four breaths gathered by God revive corpses, Ezek. 37. From a breath of air God there introduces the divine spirit into men in whom the life of the inspired air was innate. Hence in Hebrew "spirit" is represented in the same way as "breath." From the air God introduces the divine spirit, introducing the air with the spirit itself and the spark of the very deity which fills the air. The saying of Orpheus is true, that the divine spirit is carried by the winds and enters through full inspiration, as Aristotle cites in the books, *De anima*. Ezekiel teaches that the divine spirit contains a kind of elemental substance and, as God himself teaches, something in the substance of the blood. I shall explain this matter at greater length here so that you may thence understand that the substance of the created spirit of Christ is essentially joined to the very substance of the holy spirit. I shall call the air spirit because in the sacred language there is no special name for air. Indeed, that fact indicates that the divine breath is in the air which the spirit of the Lord fills.

So that you, the reader, may have the whole doctrine of the divine spirit and the spirit, I shall add here the divine philosophy which you will easily understand if you have been trained in anatomy. It is said that in us there is a triple spirit from the substance of three higher elements, natural, vital and animal. Aphrodisaeus calls them three spirits. But they are not three but once again of the single spirit (*spiritus*). The vital spirit is that which is communicated through anastomoses from the arteries to the veins in which it is called the natural [spirit]. Therefore the first [i.e., natural spirit] is of the blood, and its seat is in the liver and in the veins of the body. The second is the vital spirit of which the seat is in the heart and in the arteries of the body. The third is the animal spirit, a ray of light, as it were, of which the seat is in the brain and the nerves of the body. In all these there resides the energy of the one spirit and of the light of God. The formation of man from the uterus teaches that the vital spirit is communicated from the heart to the liver. For an artery joined to a vein is transmitted through the umbilicus of the foetus, and in like manner afterward the artery and vein are always joined in us. The divine spirit of Adam was inspired from God into the heart before [it was communicated into] the liver, and from there was communicated to the liver. The divine spirit was truly drawn into the mouth and nostrils, but the inspiration extended to the heart. The heart is the first living thing, the source of heat in the middle of the body. From the liver it takes the liquid of life, a kind of material, and in return vivifies it, just as the liquid of water furnishes material for higher substances and by them, with the addition of light, is vivified so that [in turn] it may invigorate. The material of the divine spirit is from the blood of the liver by way of a remarkable elaboration of which you will now hear. Hence it is said that the divine spirit is in the blood, and the divine spirit is itself the blood, or the sanguineous spirit. It is not said that the divine spirit is principally in the walls of the heart, or in the body of the brain or of the liver, but in the blood, as is taught by God himself in Gen. 9, Levit. 7 and Deut. 12.

In this matter there must first be understood the substantial generation of the vital spirit which is composed of a very subtle blood nourished by the inspired air. The vital spirit has its origin in the left ventricle of the heart, and the lungs assist greatly in its generation. It is a rarefied spirit, elaborated by the force of heat, reddish-yellow (*flavo*) and of fiery potency, so that it is a kind of clear vapor from very pure blood, containing in itself the substance of water, air and fire. It is generated in the lungs from a mixture of inspired air with elaborated, subtle blood which the right ventricle of the heart communicates to the left. However, this communication is made not through the middle wall of the heart, as is commonly believed, but by a very ingenious arrangement the subtle blood is urged forward by a long course through the lungs; it is elaborated by the lungs, becomes reddish-yellow and is poured from the pulmonary artery into the pulmonary vein. Then in the pulmonary vein it is mixed with inspired air and through expiration it is cleansed of its sooty vapors. Thus finally the whole mixture, suitably prepared for the production of the vital spirit, is drawn onward to the left ventricle of the heart by diastole.

That the communication and elaboration are accomplished in this way through the lungs we are taught by the different conjunctions and the communication of the pulmonary artery with the pulmonary vein in the lungs. The notable size of the pulmonary artery confirms this; that is, it was not made of such sort or of such size, nor does it emit so great a force of pure blood from the heart itself into the lungs merely for their nourishment; nor would the heart be of much service to the lungs, since at an earlier stage, in the embryo, the lungs, as Galen teaches, are nourished from elsewhere because those little membranes or valvules of the heart are not opened until the time of birth. Therefore that the blood is poured from the heart into the lungs at the very time of birth, and so copiously, is for another purpose. Likewise, not merely air, but air mixed with blood, is sent from the lungs to the heart through the pulmonary vein; therefore the mixture occurs in the lungs. That reddish-yellow color is given to the spirituous blood by the lungs; it is not from the heart.

In the left ventricle of the heart there is no place large enough for so great and copious a mixture, nor for that elaboration imbuing the reddish-yellow color. Finally, that middle wall, since it is lacking in vessels and mechanisms, is not suitable for that communication and elaboration, although something may possibly sweat through. By the same arrangement by which a transfusion of the blood from the portal vein to the vena cava occurs in the liver, so a transfusion of the spirit from the pulmonary artery to the pulmonary vein occurs in the lung. If anyone compares these things with those which Galen wrote in books VI and VII, *De usu partium,* he will thoroughly understand a truth which was unknown to Galen.

And so that vital spirit is then transfused from the left ventricle of the heart into the arteries of the whole body so that that which is more rarefied seeks the higher regions where it is further elaborated, especially in the retiform plexus situated under the base of the brain, and, approaching the special seat of the rational soul, the animal spirit begins to be formed from the vital. Again it is more greatly rarefied by the fiery voice of the mind, elaborated and completed in the very slender vessels or hair-like (*capillaribus*) arteries which are situated in the choroid plexuses and contain the mind itself. These plexuses penetrate all the innermost parts of the brain, internally girdling the ventricles of the brain, and those vessels, enfolded and woven together as far as the origins of the nerves, serve to introduce in these last the faculties of sensation and motion. Those vessels in a very remarkable way are woven together very finely, and even if they are called arteries, nevertheless they are the termination of arteries extending through the assistance of the meninges to the origin of the nerves. It is a new kind of vessels. For just as in the transfusion from the veins into the arteries there is a new kind of vessels in the lung, from vein and artery, so in the transfusion from the arteries into the nerves there is a new kind of vessels from the tunic of the artery in the meninx, since especially do the meninges preserve their tunics in the nerves. The sensibility of the nerves is not in their soft material, as in the brain. All nerves end in membranous filaments which have the most exquisite sensibility and to which for this reason the spirit is always sent. And from those little vessels of the meninges, or choroid plexuses, as from a source, the clear animal spirit is poured forth like a ray through the nerves into the eyes and other sense organs. By the same route, but in reverse, light images of things causing sensation, coming from without, are sent to the same source, penetrating inwardly, as it were, through the clear medium [i.e., spirit].

From these things it is sufficiently clear that that soft mass of the brain is not properly the seat of the rational soul, since it is cold and lacking in sensation. But it is like a bolster for the aforesaid vessels lest they be broken, and like a custodian of the animal spirit lest it blow away when it must be communicated to the nerves; and it is cold that it may temper that fiery heat contained within the vessels. Hence also it happens that the nerves serve the tunic of the membrane in the internal cavity, which is common to the aforesaid vessels as a faithful guardian of the spirit, and they hold this [away] from the thin meninx just as they hold another from the thick. Also those empty spaces of the ventricles of the brain which puzzle philosophers and physicians contain nothing else but the spirit. But those ventricles were made in the first place like a cloaca for the reception of the purgings from the brain so that they may test the excrementa received there, from which morbid defluxions arise, and provide a passage to the palate and nostrils. And when the ventricles are so filled with pituita that the arteries themselves or the choroid plexuses are immersed in it, then suddenly apoplexy is aroused. If a very noxious humor obstructs a part, and its vapor infects the mind, epilepsy occurs, or another disease, according to the part in which it settles when it has been expelled. Therefore let us say that it is the mind which we clearly perceive to be afflicted. From the immoderate heat of those vessels, or from the inflammation of the meninges, obvious delirium and frenzy occur. Whence from the diseases occurring by reason of site and substance, by force of heat and because of the ingenious construction of the vessels containing it, and from the actions of the mind apparent there, we always conclude that those little vessels must be given first consideration because all the rest serve them and because the nerves of sensation are tied to them so that they may receive their force from them. Finally, because we perceive the intellect exerting itself there when, as a result of concentrated thought, those arteries are pulsating as far as the temples. He who has not seen this thing will scarcely understand. Those ventricles were made for a second reason, that a portion of the inspired air penetrating through the ethmoid bones to their empty spaces, attracted by diastole from the vessels of the spirit, may refresh and ventilate the animal spirit contained within and the soul. In those vessels are mind, soul and fiery spirit requiring constant fanning; otherwise, like an external fire which has been covered up, there would be suffocation. As in the case of an ordinary fire, there is required not only fanning and blowing upon so that it may take fuel from the air, but also that it may discharge its sooty vapors into the air. And just as this common external fire is bound to a thick earthy body, because of a common dryness and because of a common form of light, so that which has the liquid of the body as its food is blown upon, supported and nourished by the air; thus that fiery spirit and our soul are similarly bound to the body, making one with it and having its blood as food; it is blown upon, supported and nourished by the airy spirit through inspiration and ex-piration, so that there is a double nourishment for it, spiritual and corporeal.

Servetus and His Accidental Discovery

Michael Servetus, or Miguel Servet y Reves, whom the learned Lynn Thorndike describes as "another ill-fated wanderer," began his literary career in a most unfortunate fashion. Before even reaching the age of twenty-one (around 1532), he had published two pamphlets on the Trinity, a subject reserved for the most revered and erudite theologians. Although he strongly opposed the Lutheran position, he made no friends among Catholics, and both Catholic and Protestant authorities sought to apprehend him for heresy and blasphemy, regarded at the time as heinous crimes. Seeking a hiding place, he changed his name to Villanovanus and finally took shelter in France. Relocating was no new experience to the young and brilliant scholar. He was born in Spain but had already lived and worked and made enemies and a few friends in France, Italy, Switzerland, and Germany besides his homeland.

Servetus gained an early reputation as a geographer, mathematician, and astronomer and showed an interest in medicine, although there is no evidence that he was graduated from or ever attended any medical school. His debut in medical writing occurred in 1536, when he was about twenty-five, with the issuance of a small work entitled *An Apologia Against Leonhard Fuchs*. It was an attack upon Fuchs (1501–66), a distinguished physician and botanist who had published a text in praise of Galen and Hippocrates and against the popular Arab school of medicine, dominated by Avicenna. Servetus accused Fuchs of heresy, a common charge at the time and one more serious than espionage or treason today. His next booklet, entitled *A Complete Account of Syrups Carefully Refined According to the Judgment of Galen*, was written in the true orthodox spirit of Galenworship and the medieval belief-web. The syrups he discussed were purported to aid digestion. Invited to lecture at the University of Paris, Servetus spoke on astrology's application to medicine, a controversial theme that got him into technical difficulties with the dean of the medical school. Several lawsuits ensued, as well as the publication of Servetus' *An Apologetic Discourse in Favor of Astrology*, which only generated further conflicts. Says the editor of the volume from which the excerpt is taken, "His impetuous temper, his egotism and an unpleasant bluster contrived to place him in a far from engaging position."

These writings constitute all of Servetus' medical efforts. After about twelve years of silence, during which he claimed to have practiced medicine in France, he completed his last manuscript, *The Restoration of Christianity*, which was another work on his conception of the Trinity. Making no headway, he finally began a correspondence with Calvin, the reformer of Geneva, to whom he sent his own composition plus much harsh and unsolicited criticism of Calvin's philosophy.

Calvin was aroused by the heretical ideas he found in Servetus' manuscript and notified the authorities in France, who duly arrested Servetus on the charge of heresy. For the Inquisitors in France his capture was a boon, for he had been on their list for years. He was promptly questioned and imprisoned but subsequently escaped. Although the Archbishop in charge of his case was his erstwhile friend and benefactor, Servetus was tried in absentia and found guilty "of scandalous heresy, sedition, rebellion, and evasion of prison." His punishment was to be a slow death at the stake and the consignment of his books to the flames, which verdict was executed in effigy. The only asylum open to Servetus was Italy. Possibly on his way there, he went to Geneva, where Calvin was in power. It is also possible that he went to Geneva to continue his debate with Calvin. In any event, while attending services in church, he was recognized and again arrested. He was imprisoned, tried as a heretic, convicted, mainly under Calvin's direction, and burnt at the stake on October 27, 1553.

The burning of his last book in Vienne, France, where it was published, was so thorough a job that out of 1000 copies printed, only three are in existence today. The excerpt on the pulmonary circulation derives from that work.

The basis for Servetus' particular contribution to the concept of the circulation was his concern with religion, specifically, with the statement in Genesis that God breathed the divine spirit into man as part of His task in creation. After equating spirit with breath, Servetus takes the next step and equates both with air. Thus in the midst of a recital of medieval thoughts on physiology and medicine, the idea of the pulmonary circulation bursts forth. The mind that generated the idea disputed nothing relevant, questioned not a single tenet of the old web of beliefs, and formulated no experiments, so far as is known. Servetus was an orthodox defender of the ancients and a traditional Galenist, and his dissections were conventional and perfunctory. Yet, whereas Galen left his scheme vague, unsettled, and full of contradiction, Servetus, perhaps through being less responsible or more loquacious and unhampered, messed about with ideas in such a way as to actually emerge with a wonderful new one of far-reaching merit, although of no demonstrable validity at the time. His idea, in all likelihood, stimulated further thinking immediately and served to guide science in a direction that proved to be profitable. Servetus reached a great truth by accident. He was no scientific challenger, no logician, no innovator in methodology or concepts, no dedicated experimentalist, probably not even a recognized physician. He was a rash, brash, arrogant full-time amateur debater, egotistic and undiplomatic, rootless and without devotion or loyalty to a demanding pursuit. He was in fact interested only in the enjoyment of controversy in the area most susceptible to it at the time, namely, religious interpretation. Fruitless though the arguments were on the whole, in terms of practical results, they led Servetus to a well-conceived and historically most valuable speculation. Just as the man of piety sees God's glory in the ugliest creatures and the oddest occurrences, so does the historian of science know that great scientific attainments often derive from the strangest minds, or rather from creative minds spending their energies in the strangest ways.

7. REALDUS COLUMBUS
Of Things Anatomical

[DE RE ANATOMICA]

The heart cannot possibly escape being cited as one of the important parts [of the body]; however, it is not the most important, as Aristotle thought, who located all actions in the heart because, of course, it exists as the source of the vital heat and perfects the vital spirits which are subsequently brought to their final completion in the lungs. Of this you will hear more clearly when there is reference to the lungs and the actions of the heart; it is the root of all of the arteries, their source, and origin; although the heart has been placed in the thorax by a very wise nature, it still does not occupy the middle of the thorax at all, nor is it situated in the middle of the body, as Aristotle would have it; for the umbilicus has located itself in the center of the body, just as we shall point out when we deal with the foetus.

· · · · ·

Again, Partius Neopolitanus Physicus, who swore excessively by Aristotle's words, said repeatedly that this fat around the heart which we mentioned was in no way fat at all: the most ample proof of this being, that it does not melt. But when I

From *De Re Anatomica,* Venice, 1559, Book VII (The Heart and the Arteries), pp. 175–87, translated by N. J. De Witt.

was giving a public lecture in Pisa, I melted that very same fat for a candle, which was at hand, without saying a word. When he saw this, not being able to mutter a word, he went away quietly, practically exploded.

· · · · ·

There are two cavities in the heart, not three as Aristotle thought; one of these is on the right, the other on the left; the right cavity is much larger than the left. The natural blood is present in the right, the vital in the left. Moreover, this is subject to a very beautiful observation, namely, that the substance surrounding the right ventricle of the heart is quite delicate, while around the left it is thick. And this has been brought about for the sake of balance, so that the vital blood, which is very fine, may not perspire out through it. There is a septum between these ventricles, through which almost all authorities think that a passage is open for the blood from the right ventricle to the left. So that this may occur more easily, they think that it [the blood] is rendered thin for the sake of the generation of the vital spirits. But they are wandering off on a long road, because the blood is carried to the lung by the vena arteriosa [the pulmonary artery], and is there thinned out; and then, along with the air, is taken to the left ventricle of the heart through the arteria venalis [the pulmonary vein], a fact which no one thus far has either noticed or recorded in writing; it can certainly be observed, and should be, by everyone.

· · · · ·

For, while the foetus lies hidden in the mother's womb, if we examine it, we shall discover that the vena cava is continuous with the vena arteriosa [pulmonary artery]. Therefore, insofar as it is a vein, it leads from an origin in the liver; insofar as it is arterial, from the heart, for the heart is the beginning of all of the arteries. This then advances to the lung, in order to take the blood there, by which it is nourished, and which it changes for the sake of the heart. . . .

But before we trace the path of this artery, it seems best to discuss the arteria venosa [pulmonary vein], which is attached to the left ventricle. Now, it is called arterial because it is devoted to spirits and arterial blood. But it is also called a vein for the reason that it has the body of a vein, that is, in its construction. It is quite a prominent vessel because it is distributed through the lungs much like the pulmonary artery. The Anatomists write on this subject (I should have said, by their leave), with little wisdom, that the purpose of these is to carry the altered air to the lungs, which like a little fan make a breeze for the heart to keep it cool, and which is not done by the brain as Aristotle thought.

These same [Anatomists] think then that these vessels receive some sort of fuliginous vapors which issue from the left ventricle (for that is what they call it in ignorance of languages). This comment could not be stated so as to please them. Needless to say, they think that what often takes place in furnaces also takes place in the heart, as if there were fresh wood in the heart which gave off smoke while it was being burned. And so much for the function of these vessels in relation to the opinion of other Anatomists. I, of course, believe exactly the opposite: this arteria venalis [pulmonary vein] was created to bring blood mixed with air from the lungs to the left ventricle of the heart. This is as plausible as it is entirely true; for if you examine not only dead bodies, but also living animals, you will find this artery full of blood in all cases. This would not be the case at all if it were constructed for air and, for that matter, vapors. For this reason, I cannot sufficiently wonder at those anatomists who failed to observe such an obvious and important fact, however distinguished they may wish to be considered. No! Let them be highly regarded by many like themselves. But it is sufficient for these men that Galen spoke as if to the disciples of Pythagoras. What? The fact is that some in our time swear by Galen's *Dogma On Anatomy*, so that they are bold enough to declare that Galen is to be adopted like an Evangelist, and that nothing in his writings is untrue. It is surprising how far they commit themselves in such statements and boast to the uninformed public that they are the leading anatomists.

There is no one who does not see how reprehensible this is, for indeed, who is there who never commits an error? But this is more than enough on this topic.

It must therefore be observed that eleven valve membranes are found by the orifices of the four vessels at the base of the heart. These are called trisulcae or tricuspids; that is, three at the vena cava, three again at the vena arteriosa [pulmonary artery], three at the artery called aorta, two at the arteria venalis [pulmonary vein]. Their structure, or appearance, is not the same; thus, those which are located at the vena cava and the arteria venalis [pulmonary vein] are different in form from the valves of the large artery and the vena arteriolis [pulmonary artery]. These [latter] have the form of three letters which are called C by the Latins; on the other hand, the others have the form of arrows. The function of these is remarkable; and it is with their help that we learn a great deal about those matters which lead to recognition of the function of the heart and lungs. The fact is that the usefulness of these membranes is in direct relation to their variations in form. Accordingly, the valves of the vena cava, to say nothing of those of the arteria venosa [pulmonary vein], lead out from their interior location, so that they may serve the inflow of the blood. The valves of the other two vessels appear, on the contrary, to have been made to convey the contained blood from the outside to the inside [of the body]. This is also to be noted, that the valves which flatten out from inside [the heart] are packed with certain cords, dispensed through the ventricle, which are made for the purpose of containing and strengthening them. As it happened, the great Aristotle was deceived by these and thought that these filaments were nerves; hence it came about that Aristotle left the written record that the heart was the point of origin of the nerves, and consequently of the senses and motions.

But, to return to the four vessels mentioned above: two of these are constructed so that they lead into the inside of the heart; this, moreover, results [in their conveying blood] when the heart is dilated, whereas the two others direct [blood] outside when the heart is contracted. Therefore when the heart dilates, it takes up blood from the vena cava into the right ventricle and, in addition, draws blood from the arteria venosa [pulmonary vein], prepared blood, or as we said, mixed with air, into the left ventricle. For this reason those valve membranes relax and yield to the influx, but, when the heart contracts, they close so that what they have allowed in may not flow back along the same path; and similarly, the valves of both the large artery and the vena arteriosa [pulmonary artery] close; and they provide passage to the spirituous blood which, as it comes out, is poured throughout the entire body [from the aorta], and for the natural blood which is carried to the lungs [through the pulmonary artery]. Accordingly, the fact is always such that when the heart is dilated, the valves which we have already mentioned [of the vena cava and the pulmonary vein] are opened, and the rest are closed. Accordingly, you will learn that the blood, which has entered into the right ventricle, cannot flow back into the vena cava. From this lesson, you infer that the heart cannot under any circumstances be the member in which the blood is created, as Aristotle thought, because the blood is conveyed from the vena cava, and this is to be admired and is contrived with great art. Moreover, the nervulus [little nerve], issuing from the nerve running from the left, extends to the membrane encircling the substance of the heart.

In addition, I should like you to know this with certainty, that no bone is to be found in the human heart, although in cattle, cows and horses, and in large animals of that kind, a sort of bone is shown, which in us does not exist at all. But the substance at least of the root of the large artery, toward the vena arteriosa [pulmonary artery], which seems to be cartilaginous, can in no way be called a bone, whatever Galen may say, who is to be laughed at in this respect, while he laughs at the older [anatomists] who did not describe the bone of the heart: a judgment that he deserved very much himself. However, this axiom is to be accepted in anatomy, that all arteries proceed from the heart, to the same extent that all veins proceed from the liver, all nerves from the brain. Therefore, from the left ventricle of the heart arises that artery which they call the "aorta," the mother of all other arteries, and which is quite large. Its substance is both thick and white; thick, of course, so that, first, the blood, full of spirit, may not easily escape, and second, so that it may not be choppy in its motion; that is, the artery is in continuous motion, not of itself, but because of the spirit. After the aorta has passed by the heart, it immediately gives birth to the small artery called the coronary, for the reason that it encircles the heart itself, rendering the substance of the heart alive, since it branches out in it in various directions.

·　·　·　·　·

Hence, so that the student of anatomy may enjoy the novelty and importance of the discovery, and learn when the carotid arteries arrive at the base of the skull, they are seen to enter that foramen from which the sixth nerve also issues, and which takes in the internal jugular veins; however, the two arteries do not originate here, as Vesalius assumed, more by conceiving than by observing; he would have it that the arteries enter the sinus of the dura membrana along with the jugular veins.

·　·　·　·　·

Accordingly, you will see a very beautiful network woven out of arteries, all of which proceed along the folds of those ventricles which we mentioned above, until they reach the most remote ones. These arteries have associated veins; and in their sinuses is the pineal gland. These Galen described according to their convoluted formation, as if of secondary importance. I venture, however, to say that if there is a marvelous network anywhere, this is it. I mean, you will nowhere be able to see a network of tiny arteries so admirable, twined, intertwined, and enfolded. But Galen was describing his remarkable network above the sphenoid, where that gland is located to take up all the excrement generated in the cerebrum, as if this function were ordained by nature. But that nothing wicked should be seen by good men, nature would have been subject to severe accusation if nature, which is usually a most far-sighted and keen-eyed artisan, and should be so, had established such a noble plexus, so distinguished, and so admirable, in a position, not only lowly, but as a bilge for so much excrement, not to say as a sewer! For this reason, I cannot sufficiently wonder how it could have happened that Galen, a man systematic more than can be expressed, and an exceedingly keen observer of nature, could have fallen into such serious errors and overlooked the location of the netlike plexus and described it incorrectly.

The Meticulous Anatomist

Realdus Columbus (1510?–59), or Realdo Colombo, was dissectionist to Vesalius when Vesalius was professor of anatomy at the renowned University of Padua. When Vesalius departed for the court of Charles V to be physician to the emperor, Columbus became his successor. He was in turn followed by Gabriel Fallopius, and Fallopius in turn by Fabricius of Aquapendente, the teacher of William Harvey. Columbus' place in this galaxy alone would indicate his historic position as an anatomist; but he also left behind him the work entitled *Of Things Anatomical,* upon which he labored for years and in which he declares that his accounts are based upon the examination of a thousand cadavers, thus presenting added testimony that dissection was available in his day to the qualified and eager. Columbus' book, the only one from his pen, was issued posthumously by his sons. It is a well-organized and complete text in anatomy, although unillustrated, and contains many valuable original contributions. Outstanding among these are his study of the organs of hearing and his detailed descriptions of the blood vascular system. He is cited by Harvey as one of the masters in the field.

Even this brief excerpt demonstrates that Columbus was no yes man. In the chapter, only about twenty pages long, from which it is taken, he criticizes Galen on six occasions—four times briefly, once sharply, and once at length—although he directs his harshest remarks at Galen's blind followers. Aristotle is criticized five times; Vesalius, his master, who praised him as his worthy student, six times; and Hippocrates, once. Great philosophers are rebuked once; anatomists in general, five times; and the ignorant physician, once. Galen alone is given at least once a nod of approval, and no contemporary is referred to with respect or merely mentioned. It should be noted, however, that none of the ancients is actually ridiculed or condemned. The critical comments on Galen, for example, are not intended to belittle Galen but to raise Columbus' prestige.

Some criticism of Galen was continually being voiced. Henri de Mondeville (1260–1320) was the author of one of the earliest books on surgery, entitled *Chirurgie* and written around 1316. In it he states:* "It would be an absurdity and almost a heresy to believe that God, glorious and sublime, had accorded to Galen a divine genius on condition that no mortal being after him never discovered anything new. What! Has the Lord thus abandoned part of His power! Has not God given to each of us, as to Galen, a natural genius? Miserable indeed would be our spirit if we should not know what had been discovered before us. The moderns are compared to the ancients, as a dwarf placed on the shoulders of a giant; he sees all that the giant perceives, and a little more. Therefore if we know things unknown at the time of Galen, it is our duty to tell of them in the writings."

Columbus' acerbity aside, the pervading and conspicuous feature of his writing is his attitude, that of a matter-of-fact investigator on guard against guesswork. He was not only a man of great skill as a dissectionist; he possessed as well an independent mind and was willing to follow where facts and cautious hypotheses led him.

Columbus' outlook is thoroughly Galenic. The liver perfects the nutrient blood, which its veins distribute throughout the body, while the left ventricle dispatches vitalized blood through the aorta. The liver consists mostly of condensed venous blood and is the king of the intestines, the seat of the passions. Some claim it to be the seat of animal spirit, but Columbus dismisses this view as too philosophical. Nor does he show fondness for the concept of vital spirit in the left ventricle. His concern is primarily with arteries, veins, and nerves, that is, with elements of exact anatomy. Anything conjectural he prefers, as he says, "to leave . . . to the philosophers." He automatically calls venous blood natural and arterial blood vital and accepts the existence of the septal pores.

According to Columbus, blood is thinned not in the left ventricle but in the lungs, where it is also aerated. He describes the pulmonary circulation much as did Servetus, but in a more logical context, knowing well that his is an original interpretation and seeking full credit for it. The accurate account of the blood's flow to and from the lungs is even more noteworthy here than in Servetus' text because it comes from a recognized expert in anatomy. Observe,

* L. M. Zimmerman and I. Veith, *Great Ideas in the History of Surgery,* Williams & Wilkins, Baltimore, Md., 1961, p. 145.

however, that even though he is a meticulous technician, wary of speculations, he presents no proofs but assumes that his words are convincing on their own.

The auricles are reservoirs for the protection of the vena cava and pulmonary vein. The pulmonary artery does not "arise from the heart, but from the liver." It conveys blood to the lungs to nourish that organ, but the lungs change it "for the sake of the heart." Columbus is opposed to comparing the heart to a furnace in which there is real fuel and smoke. He says rather that the pulmonary vein serves "to bring blood mixed with air from the lungs to the left ventricle of the heart." How did he know this, and what evidence did he have for it? The answer is that he simply conceived the notion and cannot and does not confirm it. He likes the idea, feels triumphant, and derides his colleagues for their slavish devotion to Galen's view. He probably never knew of Servetus' scheme, for he does not seem to be the kind of person who would read theological treatises.

His description of the valves, too, is marvelously precise. It is "with their help," he asserts, that we learn about the function of the heart and lungs. Blood is not created in the heart, as Aristotle claims; it merely passes through it. The pulmonary artery carries "natural blood," while the aorta receives "spirituous blood" to be supplied to the body. Columbus reiterates Galen's contention "that all the arteries proceed from the heart, to the same extent that all veins proceed from the liver, all nerves from the brain." He also agrees that the aorta has thick walls to prevent the escape of spirit and to smooth the pulsative beat caused by the spirit, not by the artery itself. His arguments, such as that with Galen over the "marvelous network" in the brain, usually appear petty. Columbus' entire work, then, comprises mostly old concepts, with one tiny new one in their midst. So any scientific pioneer lives largely in the old established world of values and beliefs, except for the small innovation that he introduces. Science builds its grand structure by adding fact to fact, concept to concept, tool to tool.

8. ANDREAS CAESALPINUS

Peripatetic Questions

[QUAESTIONUM PERIPATETICARUM]

QUESTION IV
AN EXTERNAL SPIRIT (BREATH) IS NOT INTRODUCED INTO THE HEART THROUGH RESPIRATION

Galen was of the opinion that there was a twofold reason for respiration in animals, the first one being the maintenance of the warm element in the heart. Respiration would bring this about in two ways: through moderate cooling attained by breathing in cold air, and through heat reduction attained by breathing out fuliginous wastes. The second reason for respiration is that the animal spirit might be nourished by the outside air, as is accomplished only by inhaling. Air comes in through the openings of the trachea, or hard artery, and passes into the veinlike artery [the pulmonary vein] running from the left ventricle of the heart into the lungs; for the openings of one are joined to the openings of the other so that there might be a passing of outside air into the heart. Aristotle, however, refutes this

From *Andreae Caesalpini, Aretini, Quaestionum Peripateticarum, Libri V,* Venice, 1571, translated by Rev. H. Brozowski, S.J.

opinion in the book *De Respiratione,* cap. 2, where he says: "We should not think that respiration takes place for the sake of nourishment, as though by air the fire within is nourished. The same would have to take place in other animals, yet fish take in not air but water. Besides, warmth does not come from breath but rather arises from humors that generate heat, as has been shown" (3, *De Generatione Animalium,* cap. 10). Heat, then, and the animal's vitality owe their existence not to air but to the nutriment flowing from the ventricle through the veins, as fire from combustibles. Further, if air were given an entrance into the ventricles of the heart, there should also be an exit; if this were the case, why would not the animal breathe out spirit and soul with the air? It is easier for spirit to escape from a confined region into the open than for it to enter a narrow and confined space from the open. Nor would the valves at the entrance block this, for the same Galen admits that together with the air exhaled, certain fuliginous wastes arise because of the heat of the heart; besides, there are only two little membranes at this entrance [the mitral valve] which do not close exactly, even though other orifices have three such. And what separation of airs or spirits, or what mixture of air remaining in the heart can here be meant? In addition, it is absurd that the wastes of a most useful nourishment should be looked down upon and expelled by nature, since nature actually does use even less noble materials.

There is also the problem of the motions involved. For since the intake of breath is done by inhaling with consequent dilation of the lung and thorax, and expulsion of fuliginous wastes by exhaling through contraction of the chest, this means that intake of spirit occurs with the dilation of the heart and its expulsion with the constriction of the heart; for the valves are so placed at the aperture that they open when the heart is dilated and close when it constricts. It is necessary then that the lung and heart dilate at the same time and constrict at the same time; or else the intake of spirit will take place while we exhale. For if it happens that the heart dilates while the lung constricts and is constricted while the lung dilates, air comes into the heart while we exhale and goes out while we inhale; this cannot be the case since these motions are opposed. Yet it is against experience to say that the heart and lung dilate and contract together, for it is in our power to regulate our respiration but not to regulate the pulsation of the heart. Besides, for those who respirate by natural instinct, respiration generally seems to occur less often than heart pulsation. Another difficulty arises in regard to the pulsation of the arteries. Of the vessels which terminate in the heart, some convey the fluid contained in them, as does the vena cava, to the right ventricle, and some, as does the venous artery [pulmonary vein], to the left ventricle, while others again carry fluid out, as do the aorta from the left ventricle and the arterial vein [pulmonary artery] nourishing the lung from the right. In the case of all of them, there are little valve membranes that aid in the performance of this function. They see to it that the incoming is not rejected and the outgoing not returned. Thus it happens that when the heart contracts, the arteries dilate and vice versa, and not together as might appear. For while the heart dilates, it wants to close the orifices leading outward so that the substance from the heart does not flow into the arteries; but while the heart contracts, there is an outflow since the membranes are wide open. If then the arteries should dilate and contract at the same time as the heart, it will happen that they will dilate when the flow of material from the heart will be halted, and they will contract when material from the same will be flowing. The impossibility of this is clear. To say that the heart and arteries pulsate at different times is to deny sense [data] in the search for [abstract] reason. But Aristotle says they pulsate at the same time in his *libello De Vita et Morte,* cap. 2: "There is a certain amount of absurdity in the idea that the venous artery [pulmonary vein] brings in spirit or breath from the lung."

He [Galen] does say, however, that it [the pulmonary vein] pulsates (7, *De Anatomicis Administrationibus*) because it arises in the left ventricle and contains spirit. This is the reason it is called an artery, even though its body is not that of an artery but of a vein. It pulsates in a twofold way: first, with the motion of the heart as do the other arteries, and second, with the motion of the lung because it receives spirits from the hard artery, the trachea; it dilates then in inhaling and constricts in exhaling. Since, however, it does not pulsate at the same time and with the same speed as the heart, it often will experience contrary motions. All these absurdities arise because he [Galen] thought dilation was a function of its faculty, so that it [the heart] might draw blood from the vena cava and spirit from the venous artery [pulmonary vein], and thought it a contradiction that it should pump fuliginous wastes into the lung and simultaneously spirit into the aorta. For this reason he is obliged to close the valve of the aorta in dilation, lest from it the spirit escape; and on the other hand, to open the same for its expulsion. Yet his reasoning is not consistent; he wants the fuliginous wastes expelled through the venous artery [pulmonary vein] though upon contraction of the heart its valves are shut. He holds also the following absurd opinion. Since the arteries are contracted and dilated by the same faculty which is transmitted from the heart through the walls of the vessels, he wishes to show that the pulse of the arteries has the same use in the whole body as respiration about the heart, namely that in dilation external air is absorbed across the arterial terminations, whereas the fuliginous wastes are expelled through the same passages. Consequently, he wants the arteries to dilate in order to be filled by the intake of substance from regions where the pores are located. It will thus happen that the arteries themselves, having their origin as they do in the heart, as is universally admitted, for the purpose of distributing vital spirit to the whole body, actually receive a minimum of that vital spirit. Far more numerous must be the host of terminal pores of the arteries, however small, through which he wishes these vessels to be filled. But if this is greater than what is obtained from the heart, dilation will not serve the goal of cooling, as he himself testifies. For what is obtained from the heart must be warm: the calefaction and absorption of heat through dilation of the arteries will be greater than the cooling process from the intake of outside air.

What may be the purpose of the pulsation of the heart? It will not be for sake of conserving heat, for this is provided by the respiration, as he himself asserts; and yet pulsation presumably provides this very heat, not wanted by the argument. Further, if it is necessary for the humor which on heating is converted into spirit or vapor to occupy a larger place, it must likewise be in the heart that distension takes place because of the warmth of the blood. In this case there is no need to look elsewhere for a distending or dilating faculty. For either this faculty will distend while the spirit is expanding by the action of the heat, or contrariwise, it will contract with the same. In the first instance, the dilation of the heart is not for the purpose of attracting anything at all, because the expansion of vapor by heat will alone enlarge the space. In the second case, the heart will constrict when the spirit expands; for if the heart is dilated by the faculty when the enlargement of the spirit ceases, its preceding contraction will have taken place while it [the spirit] was enlarging. Since this is all absurd, we are obliged to say that Aristotle held the truer view, which involves no absurdity, and the differences of the pulsations and concurrent events are better explained by him. The pulsation of the heart and arteries becomes a kind of consequence which follows from necessity the effervescence of humor in the heart by which the generation of blood is completed, as happens in other substances when boiled (*libello De Vita et Morte,* cap. 2); when the heart dilates, it is necessary that all the arteries dilate at the same time, since heat passes into them and one part cannot be filled without the whole becoming enlarged; at least this is true where vessels are continuous and are not altogether without life. For with no substance filling the space within, the base and extremities are not filled at once, because motion does not occur instantaneously; but when some spirit partly fills all the passages, then as soon as the other [air or spirit] is produced in the base, the whole necessarily dilates, for the new spirit merges with the rest; since then the whole becomes larger as soon as a part grows, one part cannot dilate without the whole dilating at the same time. Now all the arteries, as it were, form a kind of whole with the heart, a continuous vessel of perfect blood. With spirit coming into the dwelling of the body and being distributed by the particles of the blood, the swelling of the vessels necessarily ceases, which constitutes the contraction of the pulse. This occurs continuously, since the nourishment of the parts is continuous and the generation of the blood in the heart is also continuous.

The rising of the air, or spirit, is produced by heat, which event occurs not at random but with a purpose. For without this kind of enlargement there would be no distribution of nourishment into all the parts. Aristotle asserted this (2, *De Generatione Animalium*, cap. 4) as he reprobated the opinion of those who thought that a disposition of parts takes place, because by its very nature like is attracted to like. It would follow from this that all the flesh would coalesce into one and the bones likewise into one. Therefore, he showed that the parts are distinguished in generation and that in growth the same procedure is followed. There is then continuous motion from the heart into all parts of the body, because the generation of spirit is continuous, which harmonizes with its qualities of diffusion, causing it to spread rapidly into all parts, thus dispatching vitalizing food and extracting growth nutriment from the veins, through the cooperative action of little pores which the Greeks call *Anastomosim* [opening up, outlet, opening]. Finally, as the spirit gets mixed with the surrounding air, the crude matter of the nourishment remains, some of it congealed either by heat or by cold. Upon the outward flow of the spirit and the distribution of the blood into the various bodily parts, it is necessary that the vessels constrict, until a new breath again fills and distends them. This pulsation is more apparent in the arteries than in the veins because the spirit is carried by the latter. For Aristotle says that all the veins pulsate (*libello De Vita et Morte*, cap. 2). For those who speak in this manner we are not forced to close the valves of the outgoing vessels upon the dilation of the heart, for it is not dilated to attract. There is no danger lest there be a reflux from the arteries to the heart; for the motion takes place from the veins into the heart with the heat transporting the nourishment, and similarly from the heart into the arteries. Only in this way is there a flow because of the position of the valves; for the same motion opens both orifices, that of the vein into the heart and that of the heart into the artery. The membranes are placed in this way, lest at any time a contrary motion take place, which could happen in cases of violent disturbances of the soul or from other causes by which there would be a reflux of the blood to the heart; the valves resist this motion. For if these were not placed as they are, the fire of the heart would be extinguished even by a slight disturbance.

Were a contrary motion to take place, it would be as though a flame were held upside down for its progress; it would suffocate the fire because the nurture would be insufficiently prepared or more abundant than it should be. For the food should be prepared gradually and gradually be dispensed to the place of the flame. This is the kind of place the heart is; in it the aliment prepared according to nature can burn and become spirit. The veins supply the nurture, and the arteries receive the spirit of the flame. Rightly then, the mouth of the aorta is closed against the motion of the spirit back into the heart, lest by its supply the heat be suffocated. The mouth of the vein [vena cava] stands against motion from the heart, lest the flame of the heart be extinguished by the supply of food.

. . . . .

Let us return then to respiration, which, as we were saying, Aristotle asserts does not supply any nutrition to the fire, nor even any efflux of wastes as Galen thought, but only a cooling. To clarify the matter, it will be good to proceed by way of proposing a doubt. Someone will argue: If the purpose of respiration is to conserve the heat in the heart by protecting it from that corruption which is wont to take place by suffocation, it seems necessary according to *De Respiratione,* cap.

4, that an outside spirit both enter and leave the heart. For fire shut up in a place which admits no air is extinguished, as is clear from the example given by Aristotle in the book *De Inventute et Senectute,* cap. 3. For if coals are surrounded continually on all sides by a closed container [so-called suffocatory], they are quickly extinguished. If, however, one frequently removes the lid and replaces it, they remain lit for a long time. Likewise, hiding a fire under ashes gives it heat, for respiration is not prevented by a small amount of ashes, and the supply of initial heat resists at the same time the fire's extinction by the outside cold. The same process seems to happen in the respiration of animals. Besides, the spirit does not seem to sustain the heat by its coolness but by its substance. Any other substance which touches fire extinguishes it, as, for example, water and earth. It seems to burn only in air, whether the air is hot or cold, for a fire burns and lasts just as well in the cold of winter as it does in the heat of summer, as long as the same material is used. Coals, when blown over, prove this assertion, for they burn more brightly then. It makes no difference whether the air blown over it is hot or cold; for metal workers find no difference on this score, though they find that other conditions do make a big difference.

What does the blowing of air do? Its coldness does not affect the status of the heat, for water would do this better, yet great warmth is not produced by sprinkling water but only by blowing any kind of air. The substance of air then is required for the conservation and increase of fire. Further, Aristotle seems to concede the entrance of air into the heart, for in 1, *De Historia Animalium,* cap. 16, he says, "In the case of large animals it is clear that air enters the heart, although this is less evident in the case of some smaller ones." Those of the opposite view say, first, that we see fish preserve their heat not in the air nor by air, for they take in water because they lack lungs. Since then respiration means breathing in, it ought to increase the heat of the heart and not temper it by its coolness, for fire when blown upon becomes hot. Galen replies to this that even though fish live in water, they take in through their gills the air which is contained in the water. They get as much as they need for the nourishment of the spirit. Aristotle explodes this theory with many reasons in his *De Respiratione,* cap. 1, by arguing against Anaxagoras and Diogenes. We say then that air is necessary for preserving external fire not because the fire would grow cold, nor because the air becomes the nourishment of the fire, but for another reason. Since fire is the continuous transformation of wet into dry (2, *Meteorologica,* cap. 2), it continues its becoming and flowing like a stream even though this is not apparent on account of its speed. In the *De Inventute et Senectute,* cap. 3, generation is seen to be impeded when flow is impeded. This, however, is extinction brought about by decay, which is termed suffocation. A flow of this kind is impeded by placing around it some thick body, as, for example, water or even denser and moister air, such as is found in underground pits, where the flame of a lantern cannot burn. The transformation of the fire is speedier than [ordinary] flow which is checked by surrounding materials. On the other hand, when a wind blows, a flame is extinguished because it flows out more swiftly than the rate at which new fire is generated. The continuity of the flow is destroyed by the rapid motion of the surroundings of the flame, not however in the coals; for coals are heated more by blowing, the solidity of the fuel not permitting it to be destroyed by motion. On the other hand, when adjacent, packed materials such as ashes are removed, the flow is aided thereby.

We can take an example from an earthenware firepot: if a small hole is left in the pot, a large fire cannot burn in it for the hole does not suffice for the outflow of a large fire. The more wide open the aperture, the more freely the fire burns in the pot. A similar thing happens with coals, for when coarser wastes are produced in a fire, the outflow is reduced unless the fire is continually drawn off by continued blowing. This is necessary because no fire can burn except in air. Animals do not require respiration for the purpose of drawing off heat. It is necessary for the fire in animals to flow out through the arteries to satisfy this natural law and serve as nutrition for the whole body, for growth, sensation, and motion. None of these would be accomplished if the escape of its fire occurred through the locus of respiration. Nature therefore enclosed the spirit burning in the ventricles of the heart and surrounded it with thick flesh. Inside, she prepared the outflow canals covered with a twofold valve so that it would permit no outflow until it has fulfilled the tasks assigned to it by nature. Since the strength of animals consists in a certain moderate tension of the parts, if the terminal pores of the vessels had been larger, the fire would flow out more freely.

. . . . .

For the heart wishes, as it were, to be on fire so that it may prepare the coction of the blood and the continuous generation of the spirit; therefore cold harms it, for everything is warmed by its like and destroyed by its contrary. With greatest ingenuity then has nature formed the lungs for land animals and gills for aquatic animals, so that the heat of the blood can be preserved without harm to the heart. For the protection of the heart the pericardium surrounds it with a membrane, which acts as container to it as the warm blood passes to the lungs or gills and again returns to the heart, being cooled while in transit by contact with the cool air or water. Therefore the lung draws the warm blood from the right ventricle of the heart through a vein resembling an artery [the pulmonary artery] and returns it through the venous artery [the pulmonary vein] to the left ventricle of the heart. In the process of transmission it is cooled by the cool air flowing in the hard artery [the trachea], the canals running in the proximity of the venous artery, the cooling being achieved not, as Galen thought, by communications across mouths but merely by contact. To this circulation of the blood from the right ventricle of the heart through the lungs into the left ventricle of the same, [the findings] from dissection fully correspond. For there are two vessels which terminate in the right ventricle, two also in the left; of the two, one only leads inward while the other conducts outward in obedience to the construction of their respective valves.

The vessel leading blood inward into the right ventricle is indeed a large vein and is called the cava; the one conveying blood into the left ventricle from the lung is small and has only one tunic as do other veins. On the other hand, the vessel leading blood out of the left ventricle is the great artery called the aorta; its counterpart in the right ventricle is small, and it leads to the lungs and has two tunics as do other arteries.

Doctors not comprehending the purpose of this arrangement were of the opinion that the vessels got turned around in the lung, with the artery becoming a vein and the vein an artery; they designated as veins all vessels which terminate in the right ventricle, and as arteries all vessels which terminate in the left. They came up with many absurdities and suppositions to postulate a purpose. There pulsates, then, into the lung the vessel from the right ventricle; as a large artery it receives blood from the heart and its walls are constructed accordingly. The vessel to the left ventricle does not pulsate because it only conveys [blood], and its structure is like that of the rest of the veins. It happens that the membranes of its valve [the mitral valve] are only two in number, not three, because the danger from backflow is not so great; in fact, sometimes a backwash to the place of cooling might even be helpful. Rightly, the canals of the hard artery run alongside this vessel and not the other outgoing one. For this one [the pulmonary vein] being simpler and composed of one thin tunic can more readily be warmed. Besides, the dilation and constriction of the hard artery would have constituted an impediment to the pulsation of the other vessel [the pulmonary artery], had they been juxtaposed. Thus the whole system is beautifully ordered. Since it is necessary to have heat in the blood of the heart in order to bring about the perfection of the nutriment, first indeed in the right ventricle of the heart in which thicker blood is contained, then in the left ventricle where the blood is purer, blood is transmitted from the right side of the body to the left, partly through the septum and partly through the inner tissue of the lungs, for the sake of being cooled.

In the meantime, the lung can be abundantly fed; that it accommodates the whole of the blood which it receives surpasses the bounds of reason. For lung tissue would not be fluffy and light, as it indeed is, if it were to convert so great a supply of food into its own nature. Aristotle indicates that the blood of the lung is distributed to the other organs (2, *De Partium Animalium*, cap. 7) when he says that to man is given the largest brain because he possesses a heart and lung which are the warmest and most filled with blood. We have shown that the brain exists for the sake of cooling, not for cooling the organs, but to moderate the blood issuing from them to supply the senses. For this reason there is an inhaling of air through the nose reaching up to the brain, not only for the sake of smell, but also that the veins ascending the neck toward the brain should be cooled, for they lie near the hard artery by the vein heading for the brain. To possible objections there is an easy reply: External fire has a very swift generation in case of excess of heat, and therefore also a very swift outflow. For this reason it can burn only in the open air, since all other bodies impede its flow and suffocate it by their density. But since the fire of an animal is milder and burns in moister material, it can live in all humors, because its generation is slower than that of external fire. Therefore the time between the generation of one and then of another spurt is perceptible; in this interval the reduction of the pulse is evident, for the outflow is not impeded by being unexposed to the air. It is evident then that in respiration the substance of the air does not enter into the heart.

To the remark of Aristotle (1, *De Historia Animalium*, cap. 16) we say that some entry [of air] is permitted into the heart through the very thin branchings of the hard artery [trachea] which communicate with the branchings of the vein of the heart's left ventricle [pulmonary vein], as Galen noted; great efforts at retention of air would add strength to vessels stretched in this fashion. Otherwise, there would be no need for their constriction, without which no entrance of spirit into the heart would occur.

Caesalpinus Meanders, Hits, and Misses

Andreas Caesalpinus (1519–1603) was of a different cut from either Servetus or Columbus. His was what might be called the typical Renaissance mind, for his interests ranged over a vast field of knowledge and his approach to most problems was bold and original. He left his mark on botany, zoology, anatomy, medicine, mineralogy, astronomy, astrology, and even demonology through his many books. Most of them carry the term *Peripatetic* in their titles, meaning *Aristotelian,* because he regarded himself primarily as a student and interpreter of Aristotle.

Caesalpinus was professor of medicine at Pisa and later at Rome, served as the director of the Pisa botanical garden, and is best remembered for his book *On Plants* (Florence, 1583), in which he rewrote the botany of the time in the light of the voyages of discovery. Hardly a historian of botany fails to appreciate that Caesalpinus gave the science "a full and connected exposition of the whole of theoretical history. . . . Three things more especially characterise this introductory book; first, a great number of new and delicate observations; secondly, the great importance which Cesalpino assigns to the organs of fructification as objects of morphological investigation; lastly, the way in which he philosophises in strictly Aristotelian fashion on the material thus gained from experience. If this treatment has produced a work beautiful in style and fascinating to the reader, if the whole subject is vivified by it while each separate fact gains a more general value, it is on the other hand apparent that the writer is often led astray by the well-known elements of the Aristotelian philosophy, which are opposed to the interests of scientific investigation. Mere creations of thought, the abstractions of the understanding, are treated as really existent substances, as active forces, under the name of principles; final causes appear side by side with efficient; . . . the whole account is controlled by a teleology, the influence of which is the more pernicious because the purposes assumed are supposed to be acknowledged and self-evident, plants and vegetation being conceived of as in every respect an imperfect imitation of the animal kingdom."*

Here in a nutshell is a statement of the greatness of Caesalpinus, as well as a lesson in the need for a better understanding of the scientist and his mode of thought and of science as a human pursuit. Surely it is not amiss to point out that we too treat such concepts as force in physics and double bonds in chemistry as real; we frequently express the phenomenon of function teleologically; and to compare plants with animals is not, from an evolutionist's point of view, a crime. Taking all these circumstances into account, we conclude that Caesalpinus was an outstanding scientist and pioneer, despite the limitations that he shared with others active in science.

The book from which the excerpt is taken is an encyclopedic, long-winded exposition of many Aristotelian views, mainly in defense of Aristotle and in opposition to Galen. In the preceding Question 3, Caesalpinus defends Aristotle's notion that "The Heart is the Foundation not only of the Arteries but also of the Veins and Nerves." His mode of reasoning is thoroughly medieval. It is easy to see that being right or wrong on a given issue has no meaning here whatever. Any problem, no matter how simple, presents insuperable obstacles to a scholar of the period. To think outside the prevailing belief-web is humanly impossible, and the number of concepts that each argument necessarily entails and that only prolonged research and analytical thought could modify is very large. For this reason the entire effort appears hopeless.

What stirs our amazement, however, is the fact that even in this pure Aristotelian maze, the motion or circulation of the blood is taken for granted, although not in our sense. The old belief-web does not seem to allow a common flow. Just as Columbus or Galen, Caesalpinus simply cannot conceive that the blood systems might constitute one stream. Nonetheless, he is quite clear on the subject of the pulmonary circulation and the role of the heart. Moreover, the function he assigns to the lungs is wholly one of cooling, to the total disavowal of any form of aeration. It is remarkable that a few minds like his, bogged down in a mire of false conceptions, should

---

*J. von Sachs, *History of Botany*, Clarendon Press, Oxford, 1906, pp. 42–3.

hit upon even one fragment here and another there that are destined to fit together harmoniously and thus compose a solid, workable scheme. What is particularly interesting is that this time the contribution is made by an outspoken disciple of Aristotle. Surely Galen, as a physiologist, was closer than Aristotle to the modern tradition, and a defender of Aristotle should, according to the current fashion, be classified as even more reactionary than a Galenist.

HIERONYMI FABRICI

AB

AQVAPENDENTE

ANATOMICI

PATAVINI

DE

VENARVM

OSTIOLIS.

PATAVII,

Ex Typographia Laurentij Pasquati.

MDCIII

9. HIERONYMUS FABRICIUS

Valves of Veins

[DE VENARUM OSTIOLIS]

Valves of veins is the name I give to some extremely delicate little membranes in the lumen of veins. They occur at intervals, singly or in pairs, especially in the limb veins. They open upwards in the direction of the main venous trunk, and are closed below, while, viewed from the outside, they resemble the swellings in the stem and small branches of plants.

My theory is that Nature has formed them to delay the blood to some extent, and to prevent the whole mass of it flooding into the feet, or hands and fingers, and collecting there. Two evils are thus avoided, namely, under-nutrition of the upper parts of the limbs, and a permanently swollen condition of the hands and feet. Valves were made, therefore, to ensure a really fair general distribution of the blood for the nutrition of the various parts.

A discussion of these valves must be preceded by an expression of wonder at the way in which they have hitherto escaped the notice of Anatomists, both of our own and of earlier generations; so much so that not only have they never

From *Valves of Veins,* translated by K. J. Franklin, C. C. Thomas, Springfield, Ill., 1933, pp. 47–56.

been mentioned, but no one even set eye on them till 1574, when to my great delight I saw them in the course of my dissection. And this despite the fact that anatomy has claimed many distinguished men among its followers, men, moreover. whose research was conducted with great care and attention to detail. But a certain amount of justification does exist for them in this case, for who would ever have thought that membranous valves could be found in the lumen of veins, especially as this lumen, designed for the passage of blood to the whole body, should be free for the free flow of the blood: just as in the case of the arteries, which are valveless, yet, in so far as they are channels for blood, are on the same footing as veins?

But a further justification can be advanced for the anatomists. All veins are not provided with valves. The vena cava, when it traverses the trunk of the body, the internal jugulars, and countless small superficial veins in like manner, are destitute of them. On the other hand, a reasonable charge may be made against the earlier workers. Either they neglected to investigate the function of the valves, a matter, one would think, of primary importance, or else they failed to see them in their actual demonstration of veins. For in the bare veins exposed to veiw, but still uninjured, the valves in a manner display themselves. Nay more, when assistants pass a ligature round the limbs preparatory to blood-letting, valves are quite obviously noticeable in the arms and legs of the living subject. And, indeed, at intervals along the course of the veins certain knotty swellings are visible from the outside; these are caused by the valves. In some people, in fact, such as porters and peasants, they appear to swell up like varices: but here I must correct myself. It must be clearly stated that actual varices are due entirely to the dilatation of the valves and veins by too long retention and thickening of the blood at the valves; since in the absence of valves the veins would be expected to swell up and dilate uniformly throughout their length, differing thus from varices. So that hereby another and that no mean function of the valves *may* come to light, namely, a strengthening action on the veins themselves. For as in the cases of varix, with valvular in-competence or rupture as an expected finding, one always sees a greater or lesser degree of venous dilatation, one can doubtless say with safety that the Supreme Artificer made valves to prevent venous distension. Venous distension and dilatation would, moreover, have occurred readily since their coat is of membranous structure, single and delicate. And if they were to dilate, not only would the excessive accumula-tion of blood in them cause damage to themselves and the surrounding parts, and a swelling be caused, as is known to occur in cases of limb varix. There would also be a more or less defective nutrition of the parts above with the blood rushing in force, say, to a site of venous dilatation, and col-lected, as it were, in a pool. Arteries, on the other hand, had no need of valves, either to prevent distension—the thickness and strength of their coat suffices—or to delay the blood—an ebb and flow of blood goes on continuously within them. But let us, now, consider the number, shape, structure, site, dis-tance, and other characteristics of valves. It was certainly necessary to make valves in the limb veins either of large or medium calibre—not the small ones—in order, no doubt, to slow the blood flow everywhere to an extent compatible with sufficient time being given for each small part to make use of the nourishment provided. Otherwise the whole mass of blood, owing to the slope of the limbs, would flood into their extremities, and collect there, causing a swelling of these lower parts, and wasting of the parts above. That the blood flow is slowed by the valves, evident even without this from their actual construction, can be tested by anyone either in the exposed veins of the cadaver, or in the living subject if he passes a ligature round the limbs as in blood-letting. For if one tries to exert pressure on the blood, or to push it along by rubbing from above downwards, one will clearly see it held up and delayed by the valves. This indeed was the way in which I was led to an observation of such nature. Small veins, however, had no need of valves, for two reasons. First, owing to their smallness, they held only a little blood and all that suffices for them: and secondly, it was sufficient for the nutriment to delay in the larger vessels as in a fountain-head, since by this means the small tributaries also would not lack what was necessary.

In the limbs, on the other hand, there was some need of valves. The legs and arms are very often engaged in local movement; this movement is at times vigorous and extremely powerful, and in consequence there is a very large and vigorous output of heat in them. There is no doubt that with this output of heat the blood would have flowed to the limbs and been drawn to them in such an amount that one of two things would have happened. The principal organs would have been robbed of their nutriment from the vena cava, or the limb vessels would have been in danger of rupture. Either alternative would have been fraught with very serious ill for the animal as a whole, since the principal organs, such as the liver, heart, lungs and brain, had constant need of a very plenteous blood-supply. It was for this reason, I imagine, that the vena cava, in its passage through the trunk, and likewise the jugulars, were made completely valveless. For the brain, heart, lungs, liver and kidneys, which are concerned with the welfare of the body as a whole, needed to be well-supplied with nutriment, and absence of even the briefest delay was essential, if lost substance was to be restored, and vital and animal spirits, by the agency of which animals continue to live, were to be generated. If, however, by chance you see valves at the beginning of the jugular veins in man, you may say they have been placed there to stop the blood rushing in spate to the brain, and collecting therein in undue amount, in the downward position of the head. For the reasons enumerated, then, valves were given to the medium and large sized veins though not to the small ones, in the limbs, and yet were not given to the trunk of the vena cava or to the jugulars. Though indeed valves have been put in very many places, where, for instance, smaller branches leave the main stem to continue in other directions, and this is a mark of rare wisdom, the object being, I imagine, that the blood may be delayed at that point where it needs distributing to other parts; whereas, without such an arrangement, it would doubtless have flowed in mass through the single wider and straighter venous channel. Valves are present, so to speak, as intelligent doorkeepers of the many parts, to prevent escape of the nutriment downwards, until the parts above have acquired their fitting share of it.

. . . . .

The activity which Nature has here devised is strangely like that which artificial means have produced in the machinery of mills. Here engineers put certain hindrances in the water's way so that a large quantity of it may be kept back and accumulate for the use of the milling machinery. . . . Behind them collects in a suitable hollow a large head of water and finally all that is required. In like manner nature labours in the veins by means of valves, here singly, there in pairs, the veins themselves representing the channels for the streams.

Nor let anyone here be surprised that nature puts valves— frequently paired—in various places, where no branch is given off obliquely in the trunk of a vein, while nevertheless valves are required to hold back the blood somewhat and retain it. For valves are placed in veins less with a view to causing a pooling and storing of blood before the oblique mouths of branches than with a view to checking it on its course and preventing the whole mass of it slipping headlong down and escaping. A row of many valves was needed, and individual ones contributing each a little, not only to delaying the hurrying blood as already described, but also everywhere to preventing distension of the veins.

. . . Nature has therefore so placed the valves that in every case the higher valves are on the opposite side of the vein to the valves immediately below them; not unlike the way in which in the vegetable kingdom flowers, leaves, and branches grow successively from opposite side of the stem. In this way the lower valves always delay whatever slips past the upper ones, but meanwhile the passage of blood is not blocked.

Finally, a point in connection with valves needs investigation, namely, how it happens that in some people more frequent and more numerous valves are seen in both legs and

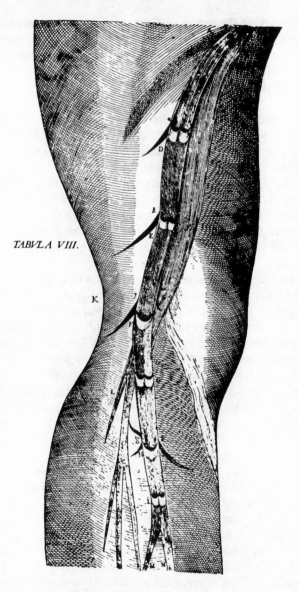

TABVLA VIII.

Leg vein, with single and double valves. The artery, to the right in the upper half of the figure and to the left in the lower half, has no valves.

124

arms, in others fewer; a fact which is very noticeable when attendants pass ligatures round the limbs in the living person for the purpose of blood-letting. It must be said that more are seen in such as have much, very thick melancholic blood, or alternatively very thin, bilious blood (in which cases there is over-functioning of the valves, either to delay the thin fluid blood in the one case, or, in the other, to prevent the thick blood from distending the vein). Or again more are seen in such as are of powerful build or inclined to flesh, and to that extent have more numerous veins, so that they need greater functioning of valves to provide blood for the oblique branches. Or have very wide vessels which demand many valves better to delay the current of blood and increase the strength of the veins. Or the parts receive long straight veins [and more valves are present] so that the length and straightness should not allow the blood to rush right along in a stream, undelayed. Or finally more valves occur if an animal is naturally rather agile in its movement. And such is the wisdom and ingenuity of Nature which by my own efforts I have discovered in this new field. The number of valves in each vein, their distribution in the tissues, and all other matters will become better known from an actual inspection of the Plates than from any written account. . . .

A Valuable Contribution,
Small and Wrongly Understood

Aside from his brief work on valves, Fabricius (1537–1619) was a highly productive and creative scientist. He made significant contributions to the field of embryology, describing the development of the dogfish, the viper, and many birds and mammals, pointing out similarities and differences and thus laying the foundations of comparative embryology. His works *On the Development of the Eggs of Birds* and *On the Formed Foetus* are remarkable achievements. He also pioneered in the study of the pregnant uterus and the fetal membranes and placenta in the human and reported on the same structures in the sheep with meticulous accuracy and fine illustrations. He was the first to publish data on the movements and the production of sounds in animals, he added considerably to the knowledge of the anatomy of the larynx and the sense organs, especially the eye and ear, and he authored several medical and surgical treatises. He attended Galileo during his illness in 1606 and again in 1608 and was honored for his highly respected work as a physician by the Senate of Venice, which created him Knight of St. Mark in 1607. Some years later Sigismund VII, king of Poland, presented him with a gold medal. Happily married, but childless, Fabricius adopted his great-niece. Subsequently a young man of noble Venetian family became amorously interested in her. Fabricius, a widower of over eighty then, and very eager to see her married, persuaded the Doge of Venice to declare her an offspring of noble birth, and so the marriage finally took place. Obviously, even scholars and physicians could climb the medieval social ladder.

Fabricius is quite right in marveling why the valves of the veins went unnoticed so long. The truth is that there were references to them before his time, but they were vague and were not accompanied by interesting explanations that fitted them into the dominant belief-web. Apparently under such conditions an isolated finding is easily overlooked.

This excerpt demonstrates the power of the belief-web over even the discoverer of facts that another mind can put to work to overthrow the prevailing thought pattern. In other words, a discovery by itself is not enough to stimulate the growth of a new idea. For Fabricius, the discovery of the venous valves merely strengthened the old notions. However, for his pupil William Harvey, the discovery of the valves, probably together with other findings, necessitated a re-examination and re-evaluation of all the theories concerning the blood, which brought about a revolution resulting in a totally different scheme for the blood in the body.

Fabricius accepts the whole Galenic set of assumptions. Venous blood conveys nutriment to all the tissues, and the valves aid in its appropriate distribution. The function of the valves is twofold. First, they prevent dangerous dilations of the veins, which might occur from a rushing of blood into regions requiring extra and prompt nourishment. Second, they prevent starvation of parts of the body that might otherwise be deprived of adequate nutrition by needier areas. Their absence in the arteries is understandable, since blood normally ebbs and flows in them by the act of pulsation. All flow of blood is from the liver and heart outward to the tissues. Some blood is melancholic, and some is bilious. Agile animals have more valves than less active animals. Key organs are furnished with veins that are valveless because they manufacture vital and animal spirits and demand an uninterrupted blood supply. Many of the beliefs held by Fabricius were shared by Harvey, who nevertheless introduced a new concept destined to have far-reaching effects, unsuspected by anyone at the time. Therefore, Fabricius' discovery led within a few years to an idea of explosive potentialities.

10. WILLIAM HARVEY

On the Motion of the Heart and Blood in Animals

INTRODUCTION

In discussing the movements and functions of the heart and arteries, we should first consider what others have said on these matters, and what the common and traditional viewpoint is. Then by anatomical study, repeated experiment, and careful observation, we may confirm what is correctly stated, but what is false make right.

. . . . .

Since the movements and structure of the heart differ from those of the lungs, as those of the arteries from those of the chest, separate functions or purposes are likely. The pulsings and uses of the heart as well as of the arteries are distinct from those of the chest and lungs. If the pulse and respiration have the same purpose, if the arteries in diastole draw air into their cavities (as commonly said) and in systole give off waste vapors by the same pores in flesh and skin, and if also in the time between systole and diastole they contain air, in fact containing at all times either

From *Anatomical Studies on the Motion of the Heart and Blood in Animals,* translated by C. D. Leake, C. C. Thomas, Springfield, Ill., 1941.

air, spirits, or sooty vapors, what may be answered to Galen? He declared that the arteries by nature contain blood and blood alone, neither air nor spirits, as may easily be determined by experiments and explanations found in his report.

If in diastole the arteries are filled by air drawn in, the greater the pulse the greater being the amount drawn in, then when the whole body is immersed in a bath of oil or water, a previously strong pulse should either become much weaker or slower, for the bath surrounding the body will make it difficult if not impossible for the air to enter the arteries. Likewise, when all the arteries, the deep as well as superficial, are distended at the same time and with equal speed, how is it possible for the air to penetrate as easily and quickly through the skin, flesh, and bulk of the body to the deeper parts as through the skin alone? How may the arteries of the fetus draw air into their cavities through the mother's abdomen and the uterine mass? How may seals, whales, dolphins, other species of cetaceans, and all kinds of fish in the depths of the sea draw in and give off air through the great mass of water by the pulsing systole and diastole of their arteries? To say that they absorb air fixed in the water and give off their waste vapors to the water is pure fiction.

If the arteries during systole exhale waste vapors from their cavities through the pores of the flesh and skin, why not at the same time the spirits said to be contained within them, for spirits are much more volatile than sooty wastes. Again, if the arteries receive and pour out air in diastole and systole, as the lungs in respiration, why not the same if cut open as in arteriotomy? In cutting open the trachea it is clear that the air goes in and comes out of the wound in two opposite directions. In cutting open an artery it is equally clear that the blood escapes in one continuous direction and that no air either goes in or comes out.

If the pulsations of the arteries cool and purify the various portions of the body as the lungs do the heart, how, as is commonly said, do the arteries carry from the heart to the separate parts the vital blood stuffed with vital spirits, which keep up the heat of these parts, nourish them in sleep, and restore them in exhaustion? How, if the arteries be tied off, do the parts at once become not only torpid, cold, and pale, but even cease to be nourished, unless it be as Galen says that they have been deprived of that heat which flowed through them from the heart? So it would seem that the arteries carry heat to the parts instead of cooling them.

Now, how may the diastole draw spirits from the heart to warm the parts [of the body and] at the same time [draw spirits] from the outside to cool them? Further, although some state that the lungs, arteries, and heart have the same function, they also say that the heart is the factory of the spirits and that the arteries contain and transmit them, denying, contrary to the opinion of Columbus, that the lungs either make or contain spirits. Then they declare with Galen that blood is contained in the arteries, and not spirits, contrary to Erasistratus.

It is clear that these opinions are so contradictory and irreconcilable that all are doubtful. Blood is to be found in arteries, and blood alone, as is plain from the experiment of Galen, from arteriotomy, and from wounds. By cutting open a single artery, as Galen states more than once, all the blood may easily be drained from the whole body in a half hour's time. The experiment of Galen referred to is this: "If you will place two ligatures around an artery and make a longitudinal incision in the portion of the artery between them, nothing but blood will be found." Thus does he prove the arteries contain blood alone. We may reason similarly. Finding the same blood in veins, tied off in a similar manner, that is found in arteries (as I have frequently noted in dead and living animals), we may likewise conclude that arteries contain the same blood as veins and nothing but the same blood.

Some authors, while trying to explain this difficulty in saying that blood is spirituous in the arteries, tacitly allow that the function of the arteries is to distribute the blood from the heart to the whole body, and that the arteries are filled with blood. Spirituous blood is none the less blood, as no-one denies that the blood, even that which flows in the veins, is filled with spirits. Even if the blood in the arteries is very gorged with spirits, it is still believable that these spirits are as inseparable from the blood as those in the veins. The blood and spirits comprise a single fluid (as whey and cream in milk, or heat in hot water) with which the arteries are filled, and for the distributing of which from the heart the arteries exist. This is nothing else than blood.

．　．　．　．　．

The arteries distend because they are filled like bladders or pouches and they are not filled because they expand like a bellows, as I have easily and clearly shown, and proved, I think, ere this. . . .

The contrary, however, is apparent in arteriotomy and wounds, the blood leaping from the artery rushes out with force, first farther, then nearer, alternately in spurts, the spurt being always during the distention of the artery, never during its contracture. From this it is obvious that the artery is distended by the impulse of blood, for it is impossible for it *per se* to throw the blood with such force while dilating,—it should rather be drawing air into itself through the wound, according to the common ideas on the functions of the arteries.

．　．　．　．　．

It is not to be supposed that the function of the pulse is the same as that of respiration because the respiration is made more frequent and powerful, as Galen says, by the same causes as running, bathing or any other heating agent. Not only is experience opposed to this (though Galen strives to get around it), when by immoderate gorging the pulse becomes great and the respiration less, but in children the pulse is rapid when respiration is slow. Likewise in fear, trouble, or worry, in many fevers, of course, the pulse is very fast, the respiration slower than usual.

These and other similar inconveniences beset the traditional opinions about the pulse and the functions of the arteries. Those maintained on the function and beat of the heart are perhaps no less involved in many tangled difficulties. The heart is commonly said to be the source and factory of the vital spirits, from which life is given to the different portions of the body, yet that the right ventricle makes spirits is denied,—it merely gives nourishment to the lungs. So it is said that the right ventricle of the heart is lacking in fishes (indeed in all animals in which there are no lungs), and that the right ventricle exists for the sake of the lungs.

1. The structure of both ventricles is practically the same. There is the same fabric of fibers, braces, valves, vessels, auricles, and both on section are filled with similar dark colored and coagulated blood. Why, then, should we imagine their functions to be so different when the action, movement, and beat of both are the same? The three tricuspid valves at the entrance to the right ventricle are a hindrance to the return of blood into the vena cava. The three semilunar valves at the opening of the pulmonary artery are placed to prevent back flow of blood. Why, then, when there are similar structures in the left ventricle, should we deny them a similar purpose, of hindering at one place the escape, at the other the reflux of the blood?

2. When the size, shape, and position of these structures are almost the same in the left ventricle as in the right, why say they are for the purpose of impeding the escape and reflux of spirits in the left ventricle but of blood in the right? The same arrangement cannot be suited to hinder in a similar way blood as well as spirits.

3. When the openings and vessels mutually correspond in size, as is clear in the pulmonary artery and pulmonary vein, why should one have a particular function, viz., of nourishing the lungs, but the other a general function?

4. How is it possible (as Realdus Columbus notes) that so much blood is needed for the nourishment of the lungs, with the pulmonary artery leading to them exceeding in size both iliac veins?

5. Again I ask, when the lungs are so near, the blood vessel to them of such size, and themselves in continual motion, what is the object of the beat of the right ventricle? And why did Nature have to add this other ventricle to the heart for the sake of nourishing the lungs?

It is said that the left ventricle draws material for forming spirits, namely air and blood, from the lungs and right cavity of the heart. Likewise it sends spirituous blood into the aorta. From this it separates waste-vapors which are released to the lung by the pulmonary artery. From the lung spirits are obtained for the aorta. How is this separation made? How do spirits and waste-vapors pass here and there without mixture or confusion? If the mitral valves do not stop the passage of waste vapor to the lungs, how do they stop the escape of air? How do the semilunars prevent the return of spirits from the aorta following cardiac diastole? Above all, how can it be said that the pulmonary vein distributes the spirituous blood from the left ventricle to the lungs without hindrance from the mitral valves, having asserted that air enters the left ventricle from the lungs by this same vessel and is prevented from going back to the lungs by these same mitrals? Good God! How do the mitral valves prevent escape of air and not of blood?

· · · · ·

To desire that waste vapors from the heart and air to the heart be transmitted by this same conduit is opposed to Nature which nowhere has made but a single vessel or way for such contrary movements and purposes.

If waste vapors and air come and go by this passage, as they do in the pulmonary bronchi, why do we find neither air nor sooty vapors when we cut open the pulmonary vein? Why do we always find the pulmonary vein full of thick blood, never of air, while in the lungs we note plenty of air?

· · · · ·

I would like to know why the pulmonary vein is built like a vein if it is destined for the transmission of air.

It would be more natural for it to be made of ringed tubes such as those of the bronchi, in order always to be open and not liable to collapse. . . .

Even less tolerable is the opinion which supposes two materials, air and blood, necessary for the formation of vital spirits. The blood is supposed to ooze through tiny pores in the septum of the heart from the right to the left ventricle, while the air is drawn from the lungs by the large pulmonary vein. According to this many little openings exist in the septum of the heart suited to the passage of blood. But, damn it [by Hercules], no such pores exist, nor can they be demonstrated!

The septum of the heart is of denser and more compact material than any part of the body except bones and tendons. Even so, supposing the pores are there, how could the left ventricle draw blood from the right when both ventricles contract and dilate at the same time? Why not rather believe that the right ventricle draws spirits through these pores from the left instead of the left ventricle drawing blood from the right?

· · · · · ·

From these and many other considerations it is clear that what has so far been said on the movement and function of the heart and arteries must seem obscure, inconsistent, or impossible to the thoughtful student. It will therefore be proper to investigate the matter more closely, to study the movement of the heart and arteries not only in man but in all animals possessing a heart, and to search out and find the truth by frequent experiments in living animals, and by constant observation.

CHAPTER I *THE AUTHOR'S REASONS FOR WRITING*

When I first tried animal experimentation for the purpose of discovering the motions and functions of the heart by actual inspection and not by other people's books, I found it so truly difficult that I almost believed with Fracastorius, that the motion of the heart was to be understood by God alone. I could not really tell when systole or diastole took place, or when and where dilatation or constriction occurred, because of the quickness of the movement. In many animals this takes place in the twinkling of an eye, like a flash of lightning. Systole seemed at one time here, diastole there, then all reversed, varied and confused. So I could reach no decision, neither about what I might conclude myself nor believe from others. I did not marvel that Andreas Laurentius wrote that the motion of the heart was as perplexing as the flux and reflux of Euripus was to Aristotle.

Finally, using greater care every day, with very frequent experimentation, observing a variety of animals, and comparing many observations, I felt my way out of this labyrinth, and gained accurate information, which I desired, of the motions and functions of the heart and arteries. From that time I have not hesitated to declare my thoughts on this matter, not only in private to friends, but even publicly in my anatomical lectures, as in the ancient Academy.

As usual, these views pleased some, not others. Some blamed me of wrong in daring to depart from the precepts and faith of all anatomists. Others wanted more information on these new ideas which were thought worthy of interest and of possible value. Finally I have consented to the requests of friends, that anyone may be made acquainted with my work. I have also been moved by the envy of some who, receiving my words blindly and with no understanding, have tried to ridicule me in public. So I have decided to publish my findings so all may form an opinion of me and of the work itself. I am pleased to do this since Hieronymus Fabricius of Aquapendente, although he has correctly and in a scholarly manner described almost all the parts of animals, has not discussed the heart.

Finally, if my work may be helpful to this phase of literature, it may perhaps be granted that I have not lived idly. . . .

CHAPTER II   *THE MOTIONS OF THE HEART AS OBSERVED IN ANIMAL EXPERIMENTS*

In the first place, when the chest of a living animal is opened, and the capsule surrounding the heart is cut away, one may see that the heart alternates in movement and rest. There is a time when it moves, and a times when it is quiet.

This is more easily seen in the hearts of cold-blooded animals, as toads, snakes, frogs, snails, shell-fish, crustaceans, and fish. It is also more apparent in other animals as the dog and pig, if one carefully observes the heart as it moves more slowly when about to die. The movements then become slower and weaker and the pauses longer, so that it is easy to see what the motion really is and how made. During a pause, the heart is soft, flaccid, exhausted, as in death.

Three significant features are to be noted in the motion and in the period of movement:

1. The heart is lifted, and rises up to the apex, so that it strikes the chest at that moment, and the beat may be felt on the outside.

2. It contracts all over, but particularly to the sides, so that it looks narrower and longer. An isolated eel's heart placed on a table or in the hand shows this well, but it may also be seen in the hearts of fishes and of cold-blooded animals in which the heart is conical or lengthened.

3. Grasping the heart in the hand, it feels harder when it moves. This hardness is due to tension, as when one grasps the fore-arm and feels its tendons become knotty when the fingers are moved.

4. An additional point may be noted in fishes and cold-blooded animals, as serpents and frogs. When the heart moves it is paler in color, but when it pauses it is of a deeper blood color.

From these facts it seems clear to me that the motion of the heart consists of a tightening all over, both contraction along the fibers, and constriction everywhere. In its movement it becomes erect, hard, and smaller. The motion is just the same as that of muscles when contracting along their tendons and fibers. The muscles in action become tense and tough, and lose their softness in becoming hard, while they thicken and stand out. The heart acts similarly.

From these points it is reasonable to conclude that the heart at the moment it acts, becomes constricted all over, thicker in its walls and smaller in its ventricles, in order to expel its content of blood. This is clear from the fourth observation above in which it was noted that the heart becomes pale when it squeezes the blood out during contraction, but when quiet in relaxation the deep blood red color returns as the ventricle fills again with blood. But no one need doubt further, for if the cavity of the ventricle be cut into, the blood contained therein will be forcibly squirted out when the heart is tense with each movement or beat.

The following things take place, then, simultaneously: the contraction of the heart; the beat at the apex against the chest, which may be felt outside; the thickening of the walls; and the forcible ejection of the blood it contains by the constriction of the ventricles.

So the opposite of the commonly received opinion seems true. Instead of the heart opening its ventricles and filling with blood at the moment it strikes the chest and its beat is felt on the outside, the contrary takes place so that the heart while contracting empties. Therefore the motion commonly thought the diastole of the heart is really the systole, and the significant movement of the heart is not the diastole but the systole. The heart does not act in diastole but in systole for only when it contracts is it active.

· · · · ·

Likewise, it is not true, as commonly believed, that the heart by its own action or distention draws blood into its ventricles. When it moves and contracts it expels blood, when it relaxes and is quiet it receives blood in the manner soon to be described.

CHAPTER III *THE MOVEMENTS OF THE ARTERIES AS SEEN IN ANIMAL EXPERIMENTATION*

In connection with the movements of the heart one may observe these facts regarding the movements and pulses of the arteries:

1. At the instant the heart contracts, in systole, and strikes the breast, the arteries dilate, give a pulsation, and are distended. Also, when the right ventricle contracts and

expels its content of blood, the pulmonary artery beats and is dilated along with the other arteries of the body.

2. When the left ventricle stops beating or contracting, the pulsations in the arteries cease, or the contractions being weak, the pulse in the arteries is scarcely perceptible. A similar cessation of the pulse in the pulmonary artery occurs when the right ventricle stops.

3. If any artery be cut or punctured, the blood spurts forcibly from the wound when the left ventricle contracts. Likewise, if the pulmonary artery is cut, blood vigorously squirts out when the right ventricle contracts.

In fishes, also, if the blood vessel leading from the heart to the gills is cut open, the blood will be seen to spurt out when the heart contracts.

Finally, in arteriotomy, the blood is seen squirted alternately far and near, the greater spurt coming with the distention of the artery, at the time the heart strikes the ribs. This is the moment the heart contracts and is in systole, and it is by this motion that the blood is ejected.

Contrary to the usual teaching, it is clear from the facts, that the diastole of the arteries corresponds to the systole of the heart, and that the arteries are filled and distended by the blood forced into them by the contraction of the ventricles. The arteries are distended because they are filled like sacs, not because they expand like bellows. All the arteries of the body pulsate because of the same cause, the contraction of the left ventricle. Likewise the pulmonary artery pulsates because of the contraction of the right ventricle.

To illustrate how the beat in the arteries is due to the impulse of blood from the left ventricle, one may blow into a glove, distending all the fingers at one and the same time, like the pulse. The pulse corresponds to the tension of the heart in frequency, rhythm, volume, and regularity. Because of the motion of the blood it is reasonable to expect the heart beat and the dilatation of the arteries, even the more distant ones, to go together. It is like inflating a glove or bladder, or like in a drum or long beam, when the stroke and beat occur together, even at the extremities. Aristotle says (*De Anima, lib.*

3, *cap. 9*), *"The blood of all animals throbs in the veins* (arteries are meant), *and by the pulse is sent everywhere at once."* And again (*De Respiratione, cap. 15*), *"All veins pulsate together intermittently, because they all depend on the heart. As it is always in intermittent movement, so they move together, intermittently."* It is to be noted, according to Galen (*De Placitis Hippocratis et Platonis, cap. 9*), that the ancient philosophers referred to the arteries as veins.

I once had a case in charge which convinced me of this truth. This person had a large pulsating tumor, called an aneurysm, on the right neck where the subclavian artery descends toward the axilla. Caused by the erosion of the artery itself, it was daily getting larger, and was distended with each pulsation by the rush of blood from the artery. Post mortem examination showed the relation of the parts. The pulse in this same arm was small because the greater part of the blood to it was intercepted by the tumor.

Wherever the motion of the blood in the arteries is impeded, by compression, by infarction, or by interception, there is less pulsation distally, since the beat of the arteries is nothing else than the impulse of blood in these vessels.

CHAPTER IV **THE MOTION OF THE HEART AND ITS AURICLES AS NOTED IN ANIMAL EXPERIMENTATION**

In addition to the motions of the heart already considered, those of the auricles are also to be discussed.

· · · · ·

Two sets of movements occur together, one of the auricles, another of the ventricles. These are not simultaneous, but that of auricles precedes that of the rest of the heart. The movement seems to start in the auricles and to spread to the ventricles. When the heart slows in approaching death, or in fishes and cold-blooded animals, there is a pause between the two movements, and the heart seems to respond to the motion as if aroused, sometimes quickly, sometimes slowly.

At length, nearly dead, it fails to respond to the motion, and it stirs so obscurely that the only signs of motion are pulsations of the auricle, as if just lightly nodding the head. The heart thus stops beating before the auricles, and the latter may be said to outlive it. The left ventricle stops beating first of all, then its auricle, then the right ventricle, and, finally, as indeed Galen noted, when all the rest is quiet and dead, the right auricle still pulsates. Life, therefore, seems to remain longest in the right auricle. While the heart gradually dies, it sometimes responds with a single weak and feeble beat to two or three pulsations of the auricles.

. . . . .

In fishes, frogs and other animals having a single ventricle in the heart, at the base of which the auricle is swollen like a bladder with blood, you may see this bladder contract first, plainly followed afterwards by the contraction of the rest of the heart.

It is only fair to report what I have observed to the contrary. The heart of an eel, of certain fishes, and even of other animals, may beat without the auricles. Even if it is cut in pieces, the separate parts may be seen to contract and relax. So even after auricular movement has stopped, the body of the heart may beat and pulsate. But may not this be characteristic of those animals more tenacious of life, whose basic humor is more glutinous or sluggish, and not easily dissipated? The same thing is noted in the flesh of eels, which continues to wriggle even after skinning and slicing in pieces.

. . . . .

Something similar is very apparent in embryology, as may be seen during the first seven days of the hatching of a hen's egg. First, before anything else, a drop of blood appears, which throbs, as Aristotle had noted. From this, with increasing growth and formation of the chick, the auricles of the heart are made, in the pulsations of which there is continual evidence of life. After a few more days, when the body is outlined, the rest of the heart is made, but for some time it remains pale and bloodless like the rest of the body, and does not throb. I have seen a similar condition in a human embryo about the beginning of the third month, the ventricles being pale and bloodless, but the auricles containing some purple blood. In the egg, when the fetus forms and develops, the heart grows also and acquires ventricles, with which blood is received and transmitted.

Whoever examines this matter closely will not say that the heart entirely is the first to live and the last to die, but rather the auricles (or that part corresponding to the auricles in serpents, fishes, and such animals) which live before the rest of the heart, and die after it.

· · · · ·

I have observed that there is a heart in almost all animals, not only in the larger ones with blood, as Aristotle claims, but in the smaller bloodless ones also, as snails, slugs, crabs, shrimps, and many others. Even in wasps, hornets, and flies, have I seen with a lens a beating heart at the upper part of what is called a tail, and I have shown it living to others.

In these bloodless animals the heart beats slowly, contracting sluggishly as in moribund higher animals. This is easily seen in the snail, where the heart lies at the bottom of that opening on the right side which seems to open and close as saliva is expelled. The incision should be made on the top of the body near the part corresponding to the liver.

· · · · · ·

There is a small squid, called a *shrimp* in English, *een gerneel* in Flemish, which is caught at sea and in the Thames, whose entire body is transparent. Placing this creature in water, I have often shown some of my friends the movements of its heart with great clearness. Since the outside of the body did not block our view, we could observe the least tremor of the heart, as through a window.

I have seen the first rudiments of the chick as a little cloud in the hen's egg about the fourth or fifth day of incubation, with the shell removed and the egg placed in clear warm water. In the center of the cloud there was a throbbing point of blood, so trifling that it disappeared on contraction and was lost to sight, while on relaxation it appeared again like a red pin-point. Throbbing between existence and non-existence, now visible, now invisible, it was the beginning of life.

CHAPTER V *THE ACTIONS AND FUNCTIONS OF THE HEART*

From these and other observations I am convinced that the motion of the heart is as follows:

First, the auricle contracts, and this forces the abundant blood it contains as the cistern and reservoir of the veins, into the ventricle. This being filled, the heart raises itself, makes its fibers tense, contracts, and beats. By this beat it at once ejects into the arteries the blood received from the auricle; the right ventricle sending its blood to the lungs through the vessel called the *vena arteriosa,* but which in structure and function is an artery; the left ventricle sending its blood to the aorta, and to the rest of the body through the arteries.

These two motions, one of the auricles, the other of the ventricles, are consecutive, with a rhythm between them, so that only one movement may be apparent, especially in warm-blooded animals where it happens rapidly. This is like a piece of machinery in which one wheel moves another, though all seem to move simultaneously, or like the mechanism in fire-arms, where touching the trigger brings down the flint, lights a spark, which falls in the powder and explodes it, firing the ball, which reaches the mark. All these events because of their quickness seem to occur simultaneously in the twinkling of an eye. Likewise in swallowing: lifting the tongue and pressing the mouth forces the food to the throat, the larynx and the epiglottis are closed by their own muscles, the gullet rises and opens its mouth like a sac, and receiving the bolus forces it down by its transverse and longitudinal muscles. All these diverse movements, carried out by different organs, are done so smoothly and regularly that they seem to be a single movement and action, which we call swallowing.

. . . . .

The motion of the heart, then, is of this general type. The chief function of the heart is the transmission and pumping of the blood through the arteries to the extremities of the body. Thus the pulse which we feel in the arteries is nothing else than the impact of blood from the heart.

Whether or not the heart, besides transferring, distributing and giving motion to the blood, adds anything else to it, as heat, spirits, or perfection, may be discussed later and determined on other grounds. It is enough now to have shown that during the heart beat the blood is transferred through the ventricles from the veins to the arteries, and distributed to the whole body.

. . . . .

The chief cause of perplexity and error in this matter seems to me to be the close connection between the heart and lungs in man. When the so-called venous artery, and arterial vein, were both seen to disappear into the lungs, it was very puzzling to determine how the right ventricle might distribute blood to the body or the left draw blood from the vena cava. This was implied by Galen in controverting Erasistratus on the origin and function of the veins, and the formation of blood (*De Placitis Hippocratis et Platonis, cap. 6*), *"You will reply that this is true, that the blood is made in the liver, and then carried to the heart to receive its correct form and full perfection. This is not unreasonable, no great or perfect work is finished at one effort, nor can it get its whole polish from one tool. But if this is really so, show us another vessel which takes the perfect blood from the heart, and distributes it, as the arteries do the spirits, to the whole body."* Thus Galen would not consent to a reasonable opinion, because not seeing a way of transit, he could not discover a vessel to spread the blood from the heart to the whole body!

I wonder what that great and ingenious man would have replied, had someone appeared for Erasistratus, or for that opinion now held by us and admitted to be reasonable by Galen himself, and had then pointed to the aorta as the vessel for distributing blood from the heart to the rest of the body? Had he said this transmits spirits and not blood, he would have sufficiently answered Erasistratus, who thought the arteries contained spirits alone. But he would have thus contradicted himself, and basely denied what he had strongly argued in his writings against this same Erasistratus, in showing by many potent reasons and by experiment that the arteries contain blood and not spirits.

The great man often agrees in this connection that "*all arteries arise from the aorta, and this from the heart, all normally containing and carrying blood.*" He says further, "*The three semilunar valves, placed at the opening of the aorta, prevent the reflux of blood into the heart. Nature would never have connected them with such an important organ unless for some great purpose.*" If the "Prince of Physicians" admits all this, as quoted in his very words from the book cited, I do not see how he can deny that the aorta is the very vessel to carry the blood, properly perfected, from the heart to the whole body.* Does he hesitate, as all after him to the present, because he could not see on account of the close connection between heart and lungs, a way by which blood might go from veins to arteries?

· · · · ·

CHAPTER VI **THE WAY BY WHICH THE BLOOD PASSES FROM THE VENA CAVA TO THE ARTERIES, OR FROM THE RIGHT VENTRICLE OF THE HEART TO THE LEFT**

Since the close contact of the heart and lungs in man has probably been a source of error, as I have said, the common practice of anatomists, in dogmatizing on the general make-

---

* The translator is here showing his strong prejudices to the extent of falsifying the text. Thus the beginning of this paragraph should read, "the divine Galen," and the beginning of this sentence, "the father of physicians." The quotation marks in the text here are not found in the original, and the implication that Harvey intended his appellation in derision, is too fantastic to consider.

up of the animal body, from the dissections of dead human subjects alone, is objectionable. It is like devising a general system of politics, from the study of a single state, or deigning to know all agriculture from an examination of a single field. It is fallacious to attempt to draw general conclusions from one particular proposition.

If only anatomists were as familiar with the dissection of lower animals as with that of the human body, all these perplexing difficulties would, in my opinion, be cleared up.

The situation is first of all clear enough in fishes, where there is a single ventricle in the heart, and no lungs. The sac at the base of the heart, doubtless corresponding to the auricle, pushes the blood into the heart, which plainly transmits it by a tube analogous to an artery. This may be confirmed by inspection, or section of the artery, the blood spurting with each beat of the heart.

It is not hard to see the same thing in other animals with but a single ventricle, as toads, frogs, serpents and lizzards. They have lungs of a sort, as a voice. I have made notes on the excellent structure of their lungs, but they are not appropriate here. It is obvious in opening these animals that the blood is transferred from the veins to the arteries by the heart beat. The way is wide open; there is no difficulty or hesitancy about it; it is the same as it would be in man were the septum of the heart perforated or removed, making one ventricle of the two. Were this so, no one would doubt, I think, how blood passes from veins to arteries.

· · · · ·

I have perceived further that the same thing is very apparent in the embryos of animals possessing lungs.

It is well known by all anatomists that the four blood vessels belonging to the heart, the vena cava, pulmonary artery, pulmonary vein, and aorta, are connected differently in the fetus than in the adult.

In the fetus a lateral anastomosis joins the vena cava to the pulmonary vein. This is located before the vena cava opens into the right ventricle of the heart, or gives off the coronary vein, just above its exit from the liver. This is a good-sized

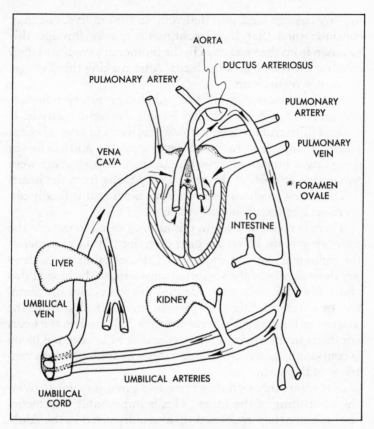

Circulation of the blood in an embryo.

oval-shaped hole opening a passage from the vena cava to the pulmonary vein, so that blood may freely flow from the one to the other, then into the left auricle of the heart, and then to the left ventricle. In this *foramen ovale,* there is a thin tough membrane, larger than the opening, hanging like a cover from the pulmonary vein side. In the adult this blocks the foramen, and adhering on all sides, finally closes and obliterates it. In the fetus, however, this membrane hangs loosely, opening an easy way to the lungs and heart for the blood flowing from the vena cava, but at the same time blocking any passage back into that vein. In the embryo, one may conclude then that blood continually passes through this foramen from the vena cava to the pulmonary vein, and then into the left ventricle of the heart. After making this passage, it can not regurgitate.

Another junction is by the pulmonary artery where it divides into two branches after leaving the right ventricle. It is like a third trunk added to these two, a sort of arterial canal passing obliquely toward and perforating the aorta. Thus in dissecting a human embryo it appears as though there were two aortae or roots of the great artery rising from the heart.

This canal gradually shrinks after birth and is finally obliterated like the umbilical vessels.

There is no membrane in this arterial canal to impede the movement of the blood in either direction. At the entrance of the pulmonary artery, from which this canal extends, there are three sigmoid valves opening outwards, so the blood flows easily from the right ventricle into this vessel and the aorta, but by closing tightly they prevent any back flow from the arteries or lungs into the right ventricle. Thus when the heart contracts in the embryo, there is reason to believe the blood is continually propelled through this way from the right ventricle to the aorta.

It is commonly said that these two great junctions are for the nourishing of the lungs. This is improbable and inconsistent, since they are closed up and obliterated in the adult, although the lungs then, because of their heat and motion, must be thought to require more nourishment. It is also false to claim that Nature had to make these passages to nourish the lungs because the heart does not beat nor move in the embryo. Nature feels no such need, for in the hatching egg, and in the human embryo, removed quickly from the uterus at an autopsy, the heart beats just as in an adult. I am not alone in often seeing these movements, for Aristotle testifies (*Liber de Spiritu, cap. 3*), "*Being part of the constitution of the heart, the pulse appears at its very beginning, as may be seen in animal experiments, and in the formation of the chick.*" . . .

From this it appears that the same thing happens in

human and other embryos in which these junctions are not closed: the heart, in its beat, forces the blood through the wide open passages from the vena cava to the aorta through the two ventricles. The right ventricle, receiving blood from its auricle, propels it through the pulmonary artery and its continuation, called the *ductus arteriosus,* to the aorta. At the same time the left ventricle contracts and sends into the aorta the blood, which, received from the beat of its auricle, has come through the foramen ovale from the vena cava.

In embryos, then, while the lungs are as inert and motionless as though not present, Nature uses for transmitting blood the two ventricles of the heart as if they were one. The situation is the same in embryos of animals with lungs, while the lungs are not used, as in those animals themselves without lungs.

. . . Nature made these ways in the embryo at a time when the lungs were not used, apparently because of the lack of a passage through them. Why is it better, for Nature always does what is best, to close completely to the passage of blood in adolescence those open ways which are used in the embryos of so many animals, without opening any others for this transfer of blood?

The situation is such that those who seek the ways in man by which blood reaches the pulmonary vein and left ventricle from the vena cava, will do best to proceed by animal experimentation. Here the reason may be found why Nature, in larger adult animals, filters the blood through the lungs instead of choosing a direct path. No other way seems possible. It may be the larger, more perfect animals are warmer and when full grown their greater heat is thus more easily damped. For this reason the blood may go through the lungs, to be cooled by the inspired air and saved from boiling and extinction. There may be other reasons. To discuss and argue these points would be to speculate on the function of the lungs. I have made many observations on this matter, on ventilation, and on the necessity and use of air, as well as on the various organs in animals concerned in these matters. Nevertheless I shall leave these things to be more conveniently discussed in a separate tract lest I seem to wander too far from the proposition of the motion and function of the heart, and to confuse the question. Returning to our present concern, I shall go on with my demonstration.

In the more perfect warm-blooded adult animals, as man, the blood passes from the right ventricle of the heart through the pulmonary artery to the lungs, from there through the pulmonary vein into the left auricle, and then into the left ventricle. First I shall show how this may be so, and then that it is so.

CHAPTER VII *THE PASSAGE OF BLOOD THROUGH THE SUBSTANCE OF THE LUNGS FROM THE RIGHT VENTRICLE OF THE HEART TO THE PULMONARY VEIN AND LEFT VENTRICLE*

That this may be so, and that there is nothing to keep it from being so, is evident when we consider how water filtering through the earth forms springs and rivers, or when we speculate on how sweat goes through the skin, or urine through the kidneys. . . .

I know there are those who deny that the whole mass of blood may pass through the lungs as the alimentary juices filter through the liver, saying it is impossible and unbelievable. They are of that class of men, as I reply with the poet, who promptly agree or disagree, according to their whim, fearful when wanted, bold when there is no need.

The substance of the liver and also of the kidney is very dense, but that of the lung is much looser, and in comparison with the liver and kidney is spongy.

There is no propulsive force in the liver, but in the lung the blood is pushed along by the beat of the right ventricle of the heart, which must distend the vessels and pores of the lung. Again, as Galen indicates (*De Usu Partium, lib. 6, cap.*

10), the continual rising and falling of the lungs in respiration must open and close the vessels and porosities, as in a sponge or thing of similar structure when it is compressed and allowed to expand. The liver, however, is quiet, it never seems to expand or contract.

No one denies that all the ingested nourishment may pass through the liver to the vena cava in man and all large animals. If nutrition is to proceed, nutriment must reach the veins, and there appears to be no other way. Why not hold the same reasoning for the passage of blood through the lungs of adults, and believe it to be true, with Columbus, that great anatomist, from the size and structure of the pulmonary vessels, and because the pulmonary vein and corresponding ventricle are always filled with blood, which must come from the veins and by no other route except through the lungs? He and I consider it evident from dissections and other reasons given previously.

Those who will agree to nothing unless supported by authority, may learn that this truth may be confirmed by the words of Galen himself, that not only may blood be transmitted from the pulmonary artery to the pulmonary vein, then into the left ventricle, and from there to the arteries, but that this is accomplished by the continual beat of the heart and the motion of the lungs in breathing.

There are three sigmoid or semilunar valves at the opening of the pulmonary artery, which prevent blood forced into this pulmonary artery from flowing back into the heart. Galen clearly explains the functions of these valves in these words (*De Usu Partium, lib. 6, cap. 10*): "*There is generally a mutual anastomosis or joining of the arteries and veins, and they transfer blood and spirit equally from each other by invisible and very small passages. If the mouth of the pulmonary artery always stayed open and Nature had no way of closing it when necessary or of opening it again, the blood could not transfuse through these invisible and delicate pores in the arteries during the contraction of the thorax. All things are not equally attracted or expelled. Something light is more easily drawn in by the distention of the part, and pushed out in contraction than something heavy. Likewise anything is more* quickly passed through a wide tube than through a narrow one. *When the thorax contracts, the pulmonary veins, strongly compressed on all sides, quickly expel some of the spirits in them, and take some blood from these tiny mouths. This could never happen if blood could flow back into the heart through the large opening of the pulmonary artery. Thus, its return through this great hole being blocked, and being compressed on every side, some of it filters into the arteries through these small pores."*

Shortly after, in the next chapter: *"The more powerfully the thorax contracts, squeezing the blood, the more tightly do these membranes, the sigmoid valves, close the opening, so that nothing flows back."* A little before in the 10th chapter: *"Unless the valves be present, much difficulty would follow. The blood would follow this long course in vain, flowing in during the distention of the lungs and filling all the vessels in it, outwards during the constrictions, and tide-like, as Euripus, flow back and forth in a way not suited to the blood. This may not seem of much importance. Respiratory function, however, would suffer, and this would be of no little significance."* Again, a little later: *"Another serious inconvenience would follow if our Maker had not provided these valves, the blood would move backwards during expirations."* So, in the 11th chapter, he concludes: *"It seems that all these valves have a common function in preventing regurgitation, appropriate to both directions, one set leading away from the heart and preventing return by that route, the other leading into the heart and preventing escape from it. Nature never wished to fatigue the heart with useless work, neither bringing anything unnecessarily to it, nor taking anything unnecessarily from it. Thus there are four openings, two in each ventricle, one of which leads into the heart, the other out of it."* A bit farther on: *"One of the blood-vessels fastened on the heart has a simple tunic, the other leading from it has a double tunic.* (Galen is referring to the right ventricle, but the same things apply to the left.) *The same cavity being provided for both of these, blood enters through the former and leaves through the latter."*

Galen proposes this argument to explain the passage of blood from the vena cava through the right ventricle to the lungs. By merely changing the terms, we may apply it more properly to the transfer of blood from the veins through the heart to the arteries. From the words of that great Prince of Physicians, Galen, it seems clear that blood filters through the lung from the pulmonary artery to the pulmonary vein as a result of the heart beat and the movement of the lungs and thorax. . . .

Since blood is constantly sent from the right ventricle into the lungs through the pulmonary artery, and likewise constantly is drawn into the left ventricle from the lungs, as is obvious from what has been said and the position of the valves, it cannot do otherwise than flow through continuously. Then, as blood constantly pours into the right ventricle of the heart, and constantly moves out of the left, it is impossible, for the same reasons as above, obviously reasonable, for it to do otherwise than pass continually from the vena cava to the aorta.

It is evident from dissection that this occurs through wide open channels in all animals before birth, and from Galen's words and what has been said previously it is equally manifest that it occurs in adults by tiny pores and vascular openings through the lungs. So it appears that, whereas one ventricle of the heart, the left, suffices for distributing blood to the body, and drawing it from the vena cava, as is the case in all animals lacking lungs, Nature was compelled, when she wished to filter blood through the lungs, to add the right ventricle, whose beat should force blood from the vena cava through the lungs into the left ventricle. Thus the right ventricle may be said to be made for the sake of transmitting blood through the lungs, not for nourishing them. It is entirely unreasonable to assume that the lungs need so much more abundant nutriment, and coming directly from the heart, so much purer and more spiritous blood than either the very refined substance of the brain, or the very brilliant and perfect structure of the eyes, or the flesh of the heart itself which is adequately nourished by the coronary artery.

CHAPTER VIII

*AMOUNT OF BLOOD PASSING
THROUGH THE HEART FROM THE
VEINS TO THE ARTERIES, AND THE
CIRCULAR MOTION OF THE BLOOD*

So far we have considered the transfer of blood from the veins to the arteries, and the ways by which it is transmitted and distributed by the heart beat. There may be some who will agree with me on these points because of the authority of Galen or Columbus or the reasons of others. What remains to be said on the quantity and source of this transferred blood, is, even if carefully reflected upon, so strange and undreamed of, that not only do I fear danger to myself from the malice of a few, but I dread lest I have all men as enemies, so much does habit or doctrine once absorbed, driving deeply its roots, become second nature, and so much does reverence for antiquity influence all men. But now the die is cast; my hope is in the love of truth and in the integrity of intelligence.

First I seriously considered in many investigations how much blood might be lost from cutting the arteries in animal experiments. Then I reflected on the symmetry and size of the vessels entering and leaving the ventricles of the heart, for Nature, making nothing in vain, would not have given these vessels such relative greatness uselessly. Then I thought of the arrangement and structure of the valves and the rest of the heart. On these and other such matters I pondered often and deeply. For a long time I turned over in my mind such questions as, how much blood is transmitted, and how short a time does its passage take. Not deeming it possible for the digested food mass to furnish such an abundance of blood, without totally draining the veins or rupturing the arteries, unless it somehow got back to the veins from the arteries and returned to the right ventricle of the heart, I began to think there was a sort of motion as in a circle.

This I afterwards found true, that blood is pushed by the beat of the left ventricle and distributed through the arteries to the whole body, and back through the veins to the vena cava, and then returned to the right auricle, just as it is sent to the lungs through the pulmonary artery from the right ventricle and returned from the lungs through the pulmonary vein to the left ventricle, as previously described.

This motion may be called circular in the way that Aristotle says air and rain follow the circular motion of the stars. The moist earth warmed by the sun gives off vapors, which, rising, are condensed to fall again moistening the earth. By this means things grow. So also tempests and meteors originate by a circular approach and recession of the sun.

Thus it happens in the body by the movement of the blood, all parts are fed and warmed by the more perfect, more spiritous, hotter, and, I might say, more nutritive blood. But in these parts this blood is cooled, thickened, and loses its power, so that it returns to its source, the heart, the inner temple of the body, to recover its virtue.

Here it regains its natural heat and fluidity, its power and vitality, and filled with spirits, is distributed again. All this depends on the motion and beat of the heart.

So the heart is the center of life, the sun of the Microcosm, as the sun itself might be called the heart of the world. The blood is moved, invigorated, and kept from decaying by the power and pulse of the heart. It is that intimate shrine whose function is the nourishing and warming of the whole body, the basis and source of all life. But of these matters we may speculate more appropriately in considering the final causes of this motion.

The vessels for the conduction of blood are of two sorts, the vena cava type and the aortic type. These are to be classified, not on the basis of structure or make-up, as commonly thought with Aristotle, for in many animals, as I have said, the veins do not differ from the arteries in thickness of tunics, but on the basis of difference in function or use. Both veins and arteries were called veins by the ancients, and not unjustly, as Galen notes. The arteries are the vessels carrying blood from the heart to the body, the veins returning blood from the body to the heart, the one the way from the heart, the other toward the heart, the latter carrying imperfect blood unfit for nourishment, the former perfected, nutritious blood.

. . . . .

Let us consider, arbitrarily or by experiment, that the left ventricle of the heart when filled in diastole, contains two or three ounces, or only an ounce and a half. In a cadaver I have found it holding more than three ounces. Likewise let us consider how much less the ventricle contains when the heart contracts or how much blood it forces into the aorta with each contraction, for, during systole, everyone will admit something is always forced out, as shown in Chapter III, and apparent from the structure of the valves. As a reasonable conjecture suppose a fourth, fifth, sixth, or even an eighth part is passed into the arteries. Then we may suppose in man that a single heart beat would force out either a half ounce, three drams, or even one dram of blood, which because of the valvular block could not flow back that way into the heart.

The heart makes more than a thousand beats in a half hour, in some two, three, or even four thousand. Multiplying by the drams, there will be in half an hour either 3,000 drams, 2,000 drams, five hundred ounces, or some other such proportionate amount of blood forced into the arteries by the heart, but always a greater quantity than is present in the whole body. . . .

On this assumption of the passage of blood, made as a basis for argument, and from the estimation of the pulse rate, it is apparent that the entire quantity of blood passes from the veins to the arteries through the heart, and likewise through the lungs.

. . . . .

But suppose even the smallest amount of blood be transmitted through the lungs and heart at a single beat, a greater quantity would eventually be pumped into the arteries and the body than could be furnished by the food consumed, unless by constantly making a circuit and returning.

The matter is obvious in animal experimentation. If an

opening be cut not only in the aorta, but even in a small artery, as Galen claims, in man, the whole blood content may be drained from the entire body, from veins as well as arteries, in almost half an hour's time.

It further appears that the greater or more vehemently the arteries pulsate, the quicker will the body be exhausted of its blood in a hemorrhage. Hence in fainting or alarm, when the heart beats slowly and feebly, a hemorrhage is reduced or stopped.

· · · · ·

Finally, it may now be suspected why no one so far has said anything to the point on the place, manner, or purpose of the anastomosis of veins and arteries. I shall now discuss this point.

· · · · ·

If a live snake be cut open, the heart may be seen quietly and distinctly beating for more than an hour, moving like a worm and propelling blood when it contracts longitudinally, for it is oblong. It becomes pale in systole, the reverse in diastole, and almost all the other things we have mentioned as proving the truth may be clearly observed, for here all happens slower and more distinctly. This especially may be seen more clearly than the midday sun. The vena cava enters at the lower part of the heart, the artery leaves at the upper. Now, pinching off the vena cava with a forceps or between finger and thumb, the course of blood being intercepted some distance below the heart, you will see that the space between the finger and the heart is drained at once, the blood being emptied by the heart beat. At the same time, the heart becomes much paler even in distention, smaller from lack of blood, and beats more slowly, so that it seems to be dying. Immediately on releasing the vein, the color and size of the heart returns to normal.

On the other hand, leaving the vein alone, if you ligate or compress the artery a little distance above the heart, you will see the space between the compression and the heart, and the latter also, become greatly distended and very turgid, of a purple or livid color, and, choked by the blood, it will seem to suffocate. On removing the block, the normal color, size, and pulse returns.

This is evidence of two kinds of death, failure from a lack, and suffocation from excess. In these examples of both, one may find proof before his eyes of the truth spoken about the heart.

· · · · ·

Some ligatures are tight, others middling. I call a ligature tight when it is pulled so firmly about a limb that the beat of the artery cannot be felt beyond it. We use this kind in amputations to control bleeding. This kind is also used in castrating animals and removing tumors, where we see the testicles and tumors dying and dropping off because the ligature keeps out heat and nourishment.

I call a ligature middling which compresses a limb on all sides, but without pain, so that the artery may still pulsate somewhat beyond the ligature. This type is used for "drawing," in blood-letting. The proper ligature for phlebotomy is applied above the elbow in such a manner that the artery at the wrist may still be felt beating slightly.

Now, let an experiment be made on a man's arm, using a bandage as in blood-letting, or grasping tightly with the hand. The best subject is one who is lean, with large veins, warm after exercise when more blood is going to the extremities and the pulse is stronger, for then all will be more apparent.

Under these conditions, place on a ligature as tightly as the subject can stand. Then it may be observed that the artery does not pulsate beyond the bandage, in the wrist or elsewhere. Next, just above the ligature the artery is higher in diastole and beats more strongly, swelling near the ligature as if trying to break through and flood past the barrier. The artery at this place seems abnormally full. The hand, however, retains its natural color and appearance. In a little time it begins to cool a bit, but nothing is "drawn" into it.

After this bandage has been on for some time, loosen it to the medium tightness used, as I said, in blood-letting. You will see the whole hand at once become suffused and distended, and its veins become swollen and varicosed. After ten or fifteen beats of the artery you will see the hand become impacted and gorged with a great amount of blood "drawn" by this medium tight ligature, but without pain, heat, horror of a vacuum or any other cause so far proposed.

. . . . .

In the case of the tight bandage, the artery is distended and pulsates above it, not below; in the mediumly tight one, however, the veins become turgid and the arteries shrink below the ligature, never above it. Indeed, in this case, unless you compress these swollen veins very strongly, you will scarcely be able to force any blood above the ligature or cause the veins there to be filled.

. . . . .

One may reason as follows. Below a medium bandage we see the veins become swollen and gorged and the hand filled with blood. This must be caused by blood passing under the ligature either in veins, arteries or tiny pores. It cannot come through the veins, certainly not through invisible ducts, so it must flow through the arteries, according to what has been said. It obviously cannot flow through the veins since the blood cannot be squeezed back above the ligature unless it is completely loosened. Then we see the veins suddenly collapse, discharging themselves to the part above, the hand loses its flush, and the stagnant blood and swelling quickly fade away.

Further, he whose arm has been bound for some time with a medium bandage, and whose hand has been rendered somewhat swollen and cold, feels, as the ligature is loosened, something cold creeping up with the returning blood to the elbow or armpit. I think this cold blood returning to the heart, after removing the bandage in blood-letting, is a cause of fainting, which we sometimes see even in robust persons, usually when the ligature is removed, or, as is commonly said, when the blood turns.

Moreover, immediately on loosening a tight bandage to a medium one, we see the veins below it, but not the arteries, swollen with blood continually carried in by the arteries.

This indicates that blood passes from arteries to veins, not the reverse, and that there is either an anastomosis of these vessels or pores in the flesh and solid parts permeable to blood. It also indicates that the veins inter-communicate, since, with a medium ligature above the elbow, they all swell up at the same time, and, if even a single venule be cut with a lancet, they all quickly shrink, giving up their blood to this one, and subside almost together.

. . . . .

The celebrated anatomist, Hieronymus Fabricius of Aquapendente, or, instead of him, Jacobus Sylvius, as Doctor Riolan wishes it, first described membranous valves in the veins, of sigmoid or semilunar shape, and being very delicate eminences on the inner lining of these vessels. . . .

The discoverer of these valves and his followers did not rightly appreciate their function. It is not to prevent blood from falling by its weight into areas lower down, for there are some in the jugular vein which are directed downwards, and which prevent blood from being carried upwards. They are thus not always looking upwards, but more correctly, always towards the main venous trunks and the heart.

. . . . .

The valves are present solely that blood may not move from the larger veins into the smaller ones lest it rupture or varicose them, and that it may not advance from the center of the body into the periphery through them, but rather from the extremities to the center. This latter movement is facilitated by these delicate valves, the contrary completely prevented. They are so situated that what may pass the horns of a set above is checked by those below, for whatever may slip past the edges of one set is caught on the convexity of those beyond, so it may not pass farther.

I have often noticed in dissecting veins, that no matter how much care I take, it is impossible to pass a probe from the main venous trunks very far into the smaller branches on account of the valvular obstructions. On the contrary it is very easy to push it in the opposite direction, from the branches toward the larger trunks. . . .

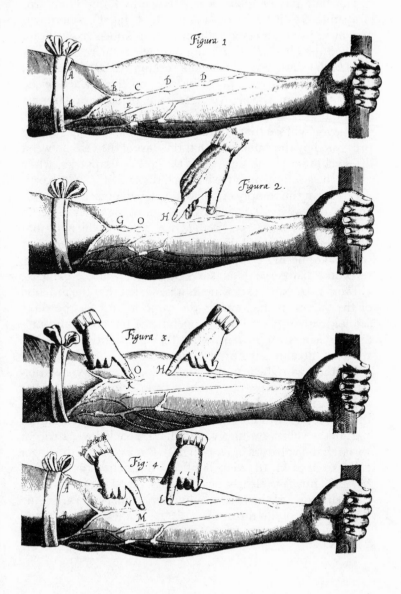

This fact may be more clearly shown by tying off an arm of a subject as if for blood-letting (*A, A,* fig. 1). There will appear at intervals (especially in rustics) knots, or swellings, like nodules (*B, C, D, E, F*), not only where there is branching (*E, F*), but also where none occurs (*C, D*). These are caused by the valves, appearing thus on the surface of the hand and arm. If you will clear the blood away from a nodule or valve by pressing a thumb or finger below it (*H,* fig. 2), you will see that nothing can flow back, being entirely prevented by the valve, and that the part of the vein between the swelling and the finger (*H, O,* fig. 2), disappears, while above the swelling or valve it is well distended (*O, G*). Keeping the vein thus empty of blood, if you will press downwards against the valve (*O,* fig. 3), by a finger of the other hand on the distended upper portion (*K,* fig. 3), you will note that nothing can be forced through the valve. The greater effort you make the more the vein is distended toward the valve, but you will observe that it stays empty below it (*H, O,* fig. 3).

From many such experiments it is evident that the function of the valves in the veins is the same as that of the three sigmoid valves placed at the opening of the aorta and pulmonary artery, to prevent, when they are tightly closed, the reflux of blood passing over them.

Further, with the arm bound as before and the veins swollen, if you will press on a vein a little below a swelling or valve (*L,* fig. 4) and then squeeze the blood upwards beyond the valve (*N*) with another finger (*M*), you will see that this part of the vein stays empty, and that no back flow can occur through the valve (as in *H, O,* fig. 2). But as soon as the finger (*H*) is removed, the vein is filled from below (as in *D, C,* fig. 1). Thus it is clearly evident that blood moves through the veins toward the heart, from the periphery inwards, and not in the opposite direction.

. . . . .

CHAPTER XIV   *CONCLUSION OF THE*
DEMONSTRATION OF THE
CIRCULATION OF THE BLOOD

Briefly let me now sum up and propose generally my idea of the circulation of the blood.

It has been shown by reason and experiment that blood by the beat of the ventricles flows through the lungs and heart and is pumped to the whole body. There it passes through pores in the flesh into the veins through which it returns from the periphery everywhere to the center, from the smaller veins into the larger ones, finally coming to the vena cava and right auricle. This occurs in such an amount, with such an outflow through the arteries, and such a reflux through the veins, that it cannot be supplied by the food consumed. It is also much more than is needed for nutrition. It must therefore be concluded that the blood in the animal body moves around in a circle continuously, and that the action or function of the heart is to accomplish this by pumping. This is the only reason for the motion and beat of the heart.

. . . . .

The blood, then, must move, and in such a way that it is brought back to the heart, for otherwise it would become thick and immobile, as Aristotle says (*De Partibus Animalium, lib. 2*), in the periphery of the body, far from its source. We note that motion always generates and preserves heat and spirit, while in quietness they disappear. So the blood, in the extremities, thickens from the cold and loses its spirit, as in death. Thus it must come back to its source and origin to take up heat or spirit or whatever else it needs to be refreshened.

We often see the extremities so chilled by a cold atmosphere that the hands, nose, and cheeks seem deathly blue. The blood in them, stagnating as in the lower parts of a corpse, becomes livid. The limbs are sluggish and are moved with difficulty, so that they seem almost deprived of life. In

no other way can they recover heat, color, and life so completely and especially so quickly as by a freshly driven flow
of heat from the source. But how can they, when heat and
life are almost gone, draw anything into them? How can
they, filled with congealed stagnant blood, admit fresh blood
and nourishment, unless they give up their old contents?
Thus the heart really is the center where this exhausted
blood recovers life and heat, as Aristotle says (*De Respiratione,
lib. 2*). New blood imbued with heat and spirit by it and sent
out through the arteries, forces onwards the chilled and
stagnant stuff, and the failing warmth and vitality is restored
in all parts of the body.

. . . . .

Further, since all animals live by food digested internally,
the distribution of this concoction must be achieved, and
hence there must be a place where the aliment is perfected
and from which it is apportioned to the separate members.
This place is the heart. . . .

Moreover, force and effort, such as given by the heart, is
needed to distribute and move the blood this way.

. . . . .

Without doubt it happens that the contagion, first being
deposited in a certain spot, is carried by the returning blood
to the heart, from which later it is spread to the whole body.

. . . . .

This may also explain why some medical agents applied to
the skin have almost as much effect as if taken by mouth.
Colocynth and aloes applied externally move the bowels,
cantharides excites the urine, garlic placed on the feet promotes expectoration, cordials invigorate, and so on. It is not
unreasonable to say that the veins take up through their
openings some of the things applied externally and carry
them in with the blood, not unlike the way in which those in
the mesentery absorb chyle from the intestines, and carry it
along with blood to the liver.

Blood enters the mesentery through the coeliac, and the
superior and inferior mesenteric arteries, and passes to the
intestines. . . .

It is not true that there are two opposite movements in

these capillaries, chyle inward and blood outward. . . . Then the total is not a mixture, but remains either wine or water. So in dissecting the mesenteric veins, chyme and blood are not found either separately or mixed, but only the same blood in color and consistency as appears in the other veins. Still, since there is some chyle or unconcocted material, however small, in this, Nature has interposed the liver, in whose winding passages it delays and undergoes more change, lest coming too quickly in the rough to the heart, it suppress vitality.

Hence there is almost no use for the liver in the embryo.

. . . . .

Why is one part formed first, another later? Concerning the origin of organs, whether one may be a cause of another, and much about the heart. Why, as Aristotle points out (*De Partibus Animalium, lib. 3*), is it the first to take shape, and [why does it] seem to have life, motion, and sensation before any other part of the body? Likewise, why does blood appear before anything else, and how does it possess the vital animal principle? How does it desire to be moved here and there, for which reason the heart seems to be provided?

In the same way, speculating on the pulse, why does one kind indicate death, another recovery? In considering all varieties of pulse, what do they signify and why? Likewise, in discussing crises, natural discharges, nutrition, the distribution of nutriment, and fluxes.

. . . . .

CHAPTER XVII *THE MOTION AND CIRCULATION OF THE BLOOD IS ESTABLISHED BY WHAT IS DISPLAYED IN THE HEART AND ELSEWHERE BY ANATOMICAL INVESTIGATION*

I do not find the heart a separate and distinct organ in all animals. Some, called plant-animals, have no heart at all.

These animals are colder, have little bulk, are softer, and of uniform structure, such as grubs, worms, and many which come from decayed material and do not preserve their species. These need no heart to impel nourishment to their extremities, for their bodies are uniform and they have no separate members. By the contraction and relaxation of the whole body they take up and move, expel and remove aliment. . . .

. . . In bees, flies, hornets, and the like, one can see with a magnifying glass something pulsate. Likewise in lice, in which, since they are translucent, you can easily watch, with a magnifying glass for enlarging, the passage of food like a black spot through the intestines.

In bloodless and colder animals as snails, shrimps, and shell-fish there is a pulsating place like a vesicle or auricle without a heart. This may be seen beating and contracting, slowly indeed, and only in the summer or warmer seasons.

In these this part is fashioned because there is need for some impulse to distribute nutriment on account of the variety of separate organs or the denseness of their substance. But the beats are seldom and sometimes entirely fail through cold. This is appropriate to their doubtful nature as they sometimes seem living, sometimes dying, sometimes showing the vitality of animals, sometimes of plants. . . . In larger, warmer, red-blooded animals there is need for something with greater power to distribute nourishment. . . .

In still bigger, warmer, and more perfect animals with more fervent and spiritous blood, a more robust and fleshy heart is needed to pump the nutritive fluid with greater force and speed, on account of the size and density of their bodies. . . .

Wherever there are lungs there are two ventricles in the heart, a right and left, and wherever there is a right there is also a left, but not the reverse. . . . The right ventricle is a sort of servant to the left, it does not reach to the apex, its walls are threefold thinner, and it is somehow joined on to the left, as Aristotle says.

• • • • •

There are also so-called braces in the heart, many fleshy and fibrous bands, which Aristotle calls nerves (*De Respiratione* and *De Partibus Animalium, lib. 3*). . . . Like the clever and elaborate arrangement of ropes on a ship, they help the heart to contract in every direction, driving blood more fully and forcibly from the ventricles.

. . . . .

In some animals the right ventricle is smooth inside while the left has these fibrous bands, as in the goose, swan, and heavier birds. The reason is the same here as elsewhere. Since the lungs are spongy, loose, and soft, not so great a force is needed to pump blood through them. . . .

So all animals, man included, that have a stronger and more sturdy frame, with large, brawny limbs some distance from the heart, have a more thick, powerful, and muscular heart, as is obvious and necessary. On the contrary, those whose structure is more slender and soft have a more flaccid, less massive, and weaker heart, with few or no fibers internally.

. . . . .

My observations previously referred to on the development of the fetus, and which Aristotle confirms in regard to the egg, throw great light on this matter. While the fetus is still soft like a worm, or, as is said, in the milk, there is a single bloody spot, or pulsating sac, as if a part of the umbilical vein were dilated at its base or origin. After awhile when the fetus is outlined and the body begins to be more substantial, this vesicle becomes more fleshy and stronger, and its constitution changing, it turns into the auricles. From these the bulk of the heart begins to sprout, although as yet it has no function. When the fetus is really developed, with bones separated from flesh, when the body is perfected and has motion, then the heart actually beats and, as I said, pumps blood by both ventricles from the vena cava to the arteries.

Thus divine Nature making nothing in vain, neither gives a heart to an animal where it is not needed, nor makes one before it can be used. By the same steps in the development of every animal, passing through the structural stages, I might say, of egg, worm, and fetus, it obtains perfection in each.

These points are confirmed elswhere by many observations on the formation of the fetus.

Hippocrates, in the book *De Corde,* did not call the heart a muscle without good reason. . . .

. . . Anatomists generally agree with Galen that the heart is composed of a variety of fibers arranged straight, transversely, and obliquely. . . .

No less should it be agreed with Aristotle in such questions on the significance of the heart as whether it receives motion and sensation from the brain, or blood from the liver, or whether it is the source of the veins and blood, and so on. Those who try to refute him here overlook or do not understand the significance of his argument. This is, that it is the first to exist, and contains in itself blood, vitality, sensation and motion before the brain or liver are formed, or can be clearly distinguished, or at least before they can assume any function. The heart is fashioned with appropriate structures for motion, as an internal organism, before the body. . . .

Many points about the arteries further illustrate and confirm this truth. Why doesn't the *arteria venosa* pulsate, since it is considered an artery? Why may a pulse be felt in the *vena arteriosa*? Because the pulse in an artery is due to an impact of blood. Why do the arteries differ so much from veins in the thickness and strength of their walls? Because they must withstand the pressure of the pumping heart and rushing blood.

Hence, since Nature makes nothing in vain, and does the best everywhere, the nearer arteries are to the heart the more do they differ from veins in structure. Here they are stronger and more ligamentous, but in their terminal branchings, as in the hands, feet, brain, mesentery, and testicles, they are so similar to veins in make-up that it is hard to tell one from another by ocular examination of their tunics. This occurs from the following good reason: the farther an artery is away from the heart the less it is reached by the cardiac pressure dissipated by the long space.

· · · · ·

Finally, why has the so-called *vena arteriosa* the structure of an artery, while the *arteria venosa* has that of a vein? Because really, in build, in function and everything, the former is an artery, the latter a vein, contrary to what is commonly believed. Why has the pulmonary artery so large an opening? Because it carries much more blood than is needed for the nourishment of the lungs.

Harvey's Discovery by Insight and Synthesis

The name of William Harvey ranks with the greatest in biology and medicine because he gave mankind a clear-cut scientific model that historically served as a springboard for further intensive investigation. This model was based not on new information that he stumbled upon or cleverly unearthed but on a thoroughly new idea. With that idea, a mass of bewildering facts suddenly fitted neatly into place within a reasonable coherent scheme. His theory was that the blood circulated, flowing from the veins, to the right ventricle, to the lungs, to the left ventricle, to the body tissues through the arteries, and back again to the veins. Others saw two blood systems performing separate and distinct functions and merging only for the sake of serving each other, and he accepted their interpretations in part. But he claimed that the two constituted one continuous stream. In consequence of his bold departure, and probably to his amazement, he discerned inconsistencies in the old concepts and read new meanings into the words of the masters of antiquity, honored in his own day by all scholars. Then, armed with his new idea, he employed his skill as dissectionist and experimenter in making new observations and performing a variety of simple tests that strengthened his original hypothesis.

It may with justice be asserted that Harvey's innovation affected only a segment of the total belief-web of the time concerning blood. He left entirely untouched notions on the meaning of pure or spirituous blood, the role of blood in heating the body, the mode of anastomosis actually shown by arterioles and venules in tissues, the meanings of chyme and chyle, the mode of their conveyance by the blood to the liver, the role of the liver in rendering the blood nutritious and that of the heart in "perfecting that aliment," the role of the lungs and the left ventricle in purifying the blood, the role of air in respiration and its mode of action in the blood, and many more phenomena that were constantly being employed as if fully understood.

He singled out one perhaps small but definitely salient and

intriguing element of the vast complex and bestowed upon it a clear, self-contained, appealing, and defensible operational pattern, which in no time at all gave rise to numerous significant experiments and opened many new lines of research, resulting in still more thoughts and discoveries of ever-increasing importance. It may well be this feature of the idea of the blood's circulation, rather than its intricacy or the ingenuity required for its conception, that makes it unique in the annals of biological science. Although many brilliant minds came close to the idea, only Harvey's reached into the medley of facts and fancies to come up with a workable scheme, and this in spite of his faith in most of the vague and baffling prevailing beliefs. Harvey, then, was no rebel defying authorities, no arrogant self-seeker, heaping abuse upon Galen and Aristotle in order to impress his own findings on stubborn and narrow-minded colleagues and ready to endure punishment in the solace of ultimate victory. In his Dedication he addresses his "learned friends" before whom he had "now for nine years and more confirmed these views by multiple demonstrations, illustrated them by arguments, and freed them from the objections of the most learned and skilful anatomists." His book was written because of "the requests, I might say, entreaties of many" of his friends. Thus he speaks to them in all sincerity and without venom. As to his attitude to the presumed tyrants and oppressors, Galen and Aristotle, he drags in a quote from Aristotle on the slightest pretext to give sanction to any claim at all, and he uses Galen's text to defend the very hub of his contribution, with never a harsh word against either.

William Harvey (1578–1657) was born in the port city of Folke-stone on the English Channel to Thomas Harvey, a merchant in trade with the Levant, and his wife. At the age of sixteen William entered Cambridge, and around 1598 he went to Padua, Italy, to study medicine in the university there, which had been made famous in the past by such anatomists as Vesalius, Columbus, and Fallopius and in his own day by Fabricius in anatomy and Galileo in physics. Galileo alone attracted many students from all over Europe. Harvey received his medical degree in 1602 and, after returning to England, continued his studies at Cambridge. In 1604 he began to practice medicine in London, where he settled after marrying the daughter of a physician.

Professional honors rapidly came his way. In 1607 he was made a Fellow of the College of Physicians, and two years later he was appointed physician of St. Bartholomew's Hospital, one of the highest medical offices in England. In 1613 he was elected one of the four Censors, or governors, of the College, in 1615 Lumleian lecturer, and in 1627 one of the examiners of new candidates. In 1618 he was appointed Physician Extraordinary to King James I, of Bible fame, and he retained that post with James' successor, the unlucky Charles I. In 1629, at King Charles' order, he accompanied a young prince on a grand tour of Europe, which gave him the opportunity to meet continental scholars. Upon his return he spent much of his time in the company of the king, who aided him in his researches and who named him his chief private physician in 1630. After the publication of his book on the blood in 1628, Harvey's work was devoted chiefly to the study of animal reproduction and embryonic development, mainly in chickens and mammals. In 1634 he was called upon to give an expert opinion in a case of witchcraft that stirred popular interest. In this and other medical situations in which he was involved, his practical judgment revealed keen common sense, scientific perspicacity, and fairness.

In 1636 Harvey went with the English ambassador to Vienna, and he took advantage of this trip to make scientific contacts, although on passing through Italy he failed for some reason to revisit his beloved Padua. After his return to England, he was caught in the meshes of the Civil War that raged from 1639 to 1649, when his friend, Charles I, was beheaded. Because of his loyalty to the king, he incurred the open hostility of antiroyalists and Parliament and lost in riots practically all his scientific notes and papers, together with all his earthly possessions. As Harvey himself put it, "Certain rapacious hands not only stripped my house of all its furniture . . . many observations, particularly on the generation of insects, have perished with the detriment, I venture to say, to the republic of letters." In spite of the turmoil, he continued with his practice of medicine and his exacting dissections until his retirement in 1645 at the age of sixty-eight.

From 1649 to 1657, the year of his death, Harvey led a rich and peaceful life, receiving acclaim both in England and abroad, to which he reacted with his customary humility and graciousness. In

1651 his second great work, *On Generation in Animals,* was published in Rotterdam under the editorship of his medical friend and admirer, Sir George Ent. This text had no dramatic or even significant effects, because the field of embryology was simply not ready for advancement. In such a situation even a genius apparently fails to make headway.

Needless to say, not everyone was pleased with Harvey's proof of the concept of the circulation. Many of the older generation were too steeped in the ancient pattern to assimilate the new or see its beauty. Nevertheless, the younger generation welcomed it wholeheartedly.

Any new idea is invariably opposed by a few individuals, who for some reason lack flexibility on the particular issue although they may be openminded and even daring in other sectors of thought. Of such a cut was the famous scholar and physician James Primerose (1592–1659), who in 1630 published in London a treatise, *Against the Thesis of Harvey.* Only the large veins have valves, he claimed, not the small ones, and the blood flows slowly in them, whereas the arteries have no valves and sustain a rapid blood flow. The valves merely strengthen the walls, and the slow movement of blood in the veins does not indicate a circulation. His facts are correct, and his reasoning is sound, but Harvey was right all the same. An Italian anatomist, Emilio Parisano, Padua-graduated like Harvey, issued a similar criticism in 1635. Two successive deans of the Faculty of Medicine of the University of Paris, Jean Riolan (1577–1657) and Guy Patin (1601–72), both illustrious physicians and anatomists, also disagreed with Harvey and defended the old belief-web. Unlike the earlier critics, they had no solid bases for their rejection but were simply verbal and contentious. Patin was actually mostly indifferent.

The great René Descartes, however, who was deeply interested in physiology, referred to Harvey in his *Discours* as "The English physician to whom we must all render a hommage of praise," while retaining some minor reservations nonetheless. Another prominent French scientist of the time, Abbé Pierre Gassendi, wrote to his colleague Mersenne in 1629 that Harvey's theory "seems very probable and well-founded." But he added, "What I object to in his work is that he imagines the blood cannot pass from the right ventricle of the heart to the left by the septum, for I remember that the Sieur Payen (a cunning surgeon of Aix) showed us, some years ago, that there existed not only pores, but open channels." Of course, such may sometimes be the case. Clearly it is not easy for a new idea to gain a secure footing.

Johann Vesling (1598–1649), professor at Pavia and the author of *A Handbook in Anatomy* (1647), advanced a reasonable argument against Harvey's scheme. Since the blood in the arteries has a brighter color than the blood in the veins, he asked, how could the two streams possibly be part of one circulatory system? Harvey answered this question in his Second Letter to Jean Riolan by stating that arterial and venous bloods were indeed alike, for each clots "with almost the same coloration and practically the same consistence, expresses its serum similarly." Such evidence, he says, "should stop some folk from going sleepless over the problem and prove that the blood looks alike in both the left and right ventricle." He denies that arterial blood is especially spirituous, asserting that "the spirits escaping through the veins or arteries are no more separate from the blood than is a flame from its inflammable vapor," and concludes that "the same blood is present in the arteries as in the veins even if it is admittedly more spirituous and more heavily endowed in the former with vital force." Thus he dismisses the two-color consideration, which endangers his theory.

Poor Harvey is obliged to react similarly to another imaginary threat. Casparo Aselli (1581–1626) discovered the lacteal vessels in the fine walls of the intestines and the peritoneal mesentery of a dog. These threadlike ducts, filled with a milky liquid consisting of fatty substances, are best seen directly after a heavy meal. Vesling studied them in detail, and Jean Pecquet (1622–74) and Thomas Bartholin (1616–80) showed that they joined another set of vessels, the lymphatics, containing clear liquid, and that the merged contents poured into the venous blood stream in the upper chest region. Harvey wrote that he had noticed the lacteal vessels but that he doubted that they contain chyle, or digested food, which indeed they do not. They only transport its fatty component. Harvey's grounds for uncertainty are rational instead of factual, in an area where data are needed and little else. Many of his objections are irrelevant. Only mesenteric veins, he maintains, carry chyle. So it is in the chick embryo, which derives its nourishment, conveyed by the blood, from the egg's albumen and yolk, and so it is also in the grown bird. Thus the circulation negotiates the distribution of digested food, and the lacteals are not important. Since he feels that they negate or weaken his model, he tends to brush them aside, as a nuisance.

A novel idea often creates strange friends and stranger antagonists. Harvey found a staunch supporter in Louis XIV, the grand monarch of France, whose physician, Dionis, urged him to defend Harvey against the influential and legally sanctioned Faculty of Medicine of Paris, which "had ostracized the new doctrine." The Faculty, which claimed the exclusive right to lecture in the field of anatomy, had abolished a chair in anatomy at the Botanical Garden, with lectures intended to bring science to the populace. Dionis encouraged the king to set up a new chair in anatomy at the Garden, for the exclusive teaching of the theory of the circulation. This action involved the king in a battle with the Faculty, which resorted to the high court, or Parlement, and won the case. Fortunately, however, Louis was quite an autocrat, and the lectures on Harvey continued with public demonstrations for "a period of 8 years." Dionis has the highest praise for Harvey and his theory but remarks in his book, "Nonetheless, we must say that this hypothesis is contrary both to reason and to experiment, but at this we should not be astonished. He (Harvey) did not know enough about the structure of the heart, and his meditations (speculations) took up so much of his time that he was not able to obtain any great knowledge of that structure." On the other hand, ten years after the appearance of Harvey's masterpiece, Alexander Reid, a cultured man who helped free four women accused of witchcraft and who would therefore not be suspected of prejudice, issued a new edition of his *Manual of Anatomy* in which the old belief-web is expounded and, oddly, there is no mention of Harvey or the circulation.

The spirit of the times was with Harvey, however, and the feeble voices of the opposition soon died out. The impact of the new idea on the social conscience was overwhelming. Historically blood had been surrounded by an aura of mystery and, as in the Bible, regarded as the soul, the essence of life. With the work of Harvey, much of the mystery was dispelled. What had been presumed to be spirit was actually a fluid, driven through a system of vessels by a rhythmically contracting and dilating organ of muscle tissue, with valves and sluices to aid the flow and joints and mouths to complete the circuit. The picture of the heart as a mechanistic pump controlling the circulation of the blood marked the dawn of scientific materialism in the West.

11. MARCELLO MALPIGHI

Epistle I (to Giovanni Borelli)

These small bladders [in the lungs] have a similar position and linking-together, so that from the trachea there is an immediate open access into both lobes, on one side and the other, and finally they come to an end, in the continuous membrane. Observation demonstrates this in lungs recently removed from animals, which, when inflated with air, appear semitransparent and exhibit a very great number of tiny bladders filled with air on their outer surfaces; it is also possible to observe these bladders in a cross section of the lung, although they are smaller and less easy to observe; they are found more easily, fortunately, in a lung which has been inflated and quickly dried out, because as they extend inward they appear as minute circles or holes, in sections made in any direction, with sinuous branches formed of a delicate and pervasive membrane; and in order to transform one's mental reservations to certainty of belief, one may remove the lung from a living animal, and by forcing water through a tube into the pulmonary artery, one can expel all the blood and wash out the pulmonary veins

From *De Pulmonibus,* Bononia, 1661, Epistle I (Pulmonary Structure and Function), translated by N. J. DeWitt.

by passing water through them; immediately one will render virtually white and transparent the entire substance of the lung reached by the water and exhausted of blood. Similarly, if first a slight pressure is applied, so that the water already absorbed is squeezed out, the air is immediately forced in through the trachea so that the lung is inflated, and then dried out in either shade or sunlight, it not only displays those transparent spherules when exposed to light but also, when cut open, reveals a white mass of tiny bladders to the naked eye. . . .

Reason can bring assistance to the weakness of the senses, by suggesting that air, which forces its way into the lungs from the trachea, requires a continuous passage for free and direct channels in and out, wherefore perhaps that internal wall of the trachea, ending as it does in sinuses and bladders, actually forms a mass of vesicles very much like a shapeless common sponge, which structure is also discernible in the dried-out lung by its particular substance, color, and brightness and is visible equally in a section of the terminations of the ramifications of the trachea and in the attached orbicules and sinuses. . . .

But here is a problem that presents itself for investigation: I mean that in the extremities of the lungs, when they are held up to the light, a certain remarkable network is seen to extend, which by its pervasive ramifications, you might say, the individual vesicles became extended and interconnected; this network is also, albeit less clearly, to be observed in the interior of the dissected lung; I am in doubt as to whether this network is composed of blood vessels, or some sort of nerve extended into vesicles, or the membranous walls themselves of the vesicles ending in the external covering membrane, because, when in a dried-out condition the interior or immediate sections are lightly scraped with a knife, certain nervous extensions of this network are seen to remain, and in the external ones there seems to be observable at close range a certain brightness, as of a nervelike substance; . . . .

I have noted, however, a much more remarkable and

deeper division, namely, that the mass of the lungs [also] consists of vesicles which are most infinitely small, being surrounded by their special membrane, provided with interconnecting passages, and running parallel to branches of the rough artery; moreover, the vesicles can be distinguished when the partially inflated lung is held up to the rays of the sun or a light; for then certain interstitial spaces, half transparent, stand out. If you explore these spaces by delicate incisions, you will isolate the vesicles on both sides as they adhere to the vessels of the rough artery; and you will find that the vesicles are interlinked by joints in their own walls when air is breathed in through the trachea.

· · · · ·

The interstices [spaces] are of appropriate dimensions, when they are offset from the vesicles in place, which, in the case of the larger animals, virtually equal the width of half a finger in cross section. I think that these interstices were produced by nature, not only to mark the boundaries and junctions of the vesicles, but also perhaps, that by taking air in, they should enlarge the surrounding vesicles in all directions, and thus multiply the pressure and consequently aid in the mixing of the mass of the blood.

Epistle II (*to Giovanni Borelli*)

And now, most famous man, I will handle the matter more closely. There were two things which, in my epistle about observations on the lungs, I left as doubtful and to be investigated with more exact study.

(1) The first was what may be the network described therein, where certain bladders and sinuses are bound together in a certain way in the lungs.

(2) The other was whether the vessels of the lungs are connected by mutual anastomosis, or gape into the common substance of the lungs and sinuses.

 • • • • •

Observations by means of the microscope will reveal more wonderful things than those viewed in regard to mere structure and connexion: for while the heart is still beating the contrary (i.e., in opposite directions in the different vessels) movement of the blood is observed in the vessels—though with difficulty—so that the circulation of the blood is clearly exposed. This is more clearly recognized in the mesentery and in the other great veins contained in the abdomen.

Thus by this impulse the blood is driven

From *Proceedings of the Royal Society of Medicine,* **23,** 7 (1929), translated by James Young, M.D.

in very small [streams] through the arteries like a flood into the several cells, one or other branch clearly passing through or ending there. Thus blood, much divided, cuts off its red colour, and, carried round in a winding way is poured out on all sides till at length it may reach the walls, the angles, and the absorbing branches of the veins.

The power of the eye could not be extended further in the opened living animal, hence I had believed that this body of the blood breaks into the empty space, and is collected again by a gaping vessel and by the structure of the walls. The tortuous and diffused motion of the blood in divers directions, and its union at a determinate place offered a handle to this. But the dried lung of the frog made my belief dubious. This lung had, by chance, preserved the redness of the blood in (what afterwards proved to be) the smallest vessels, where by means of a more perfect lens, no more there met the eye the points forming the skin called Sagrino, but vessels mingled annularly. And, so great is the divarication of these vessels as they go out, here from a vein, there from an artery, that order is no longer preserved, but a network appears made up of the prolongations of both vessels. This network occupies not only the whole floor, but extends also to the walls, and is attached to the outgoing vessel, as I could see with greater difficulty but more abundantly in the oblong lung of a tortoise, which is similarly membranous and transparent. Here it was clear to sense that the blood flows away through the tortuous vessels, that it is not poured into spaces but always works through tubules, and is dispersed by the multiplex winding of the vessels. Nor is it a new practice of Nature to join together the extremities of vessels, since the same holds in the intestines and other parts; nay, what seems more wonderful, she joins the upper and the lower ends of veins to one another by visible anastomosis, as the most learned Fallopius has very well observed.

But in order that you may more easily get hold of what I have said, and follow it with your own sight, tie with a thread, just where it joins the heart, the projecting swollen lung of an opened frog while it is bathed on every side with abundant

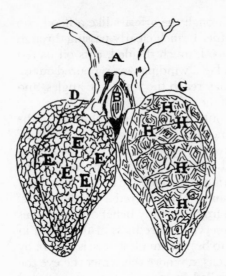

Lungs of a frog, with the trachea attached: A, larynx; B, opening of the trachea; D, external part of the right lung; E, network extension of the pulmonary artery; G, left lung cut through the middle; H, network extension of the pulmonary vein.

blood. This, when dried, will preserve the vessels turgid with blood. You will see this very well if you examine it by the microscope of one lens against the horizontal sun. Or you may institute another method of seeing these things. Place the lung on a crystal plate illuminated below through a tube by a lighted candle. To it bring a microscope of two lenses, and thus the vessels distributed in a ring-like fashion will be disclosed to you. By the same arrangement of the instruments and light, you will observe the movement of the blood through the vessels in question. You will yourself be able to contrive it by different degrees of light, which escape description by the pen. About the movement of the blood, however, one thing shows itself, worthy of your speculation. The auricle and the heart being ligatured, and thus deprived of motion and the impulse which might be derived from the heart into the connected vessels, the blood is still moved by the veins toward the heart so that it distends the vessels by its effort and copious flow. This lasts several hours. At the end, however, especially if it is exposed to the solar rays, it is agitated, not by the same continued motion, but, as if impelled by changing impulses, it advances and recedes fluctuating along the same way. This takes place when the heart and auricle are removed from the body.

From these things, therefore, as to the first problems to be solved, from analogy and the simplicity which Nature uses in all her operations, it can be inferred that that network which formerly I believed to be nervous in nature, mingled in the bladder and sinuses, is [really] a vessel carrying the body of blood thither or carrying it away. Also that, although in the lungs of perfect animals the vessels seem sometimes to gape and end in the midst of the network of rings, nevertheless, it is likely that, as in the cells of frogs and tortoise, that vessel is prolonged further into small vessels in the form of a network, and these escape the senses on account of their exquisite smallness.

Also from these things can be solved with the greatest of probability the question of the mutual union and anastomosis of the vessels. For if Nature turns the blood about in vessels, and combines the ends of the vessels in a network, it is likely that in other cases an anastomosis joins them; this is clearly recognized in the bladder of frogs swollen with urine, in which the above described motion of the blood is observed through the transparent vessels joined together by anastomosis, and not that those vessels have received that connexion and course which the veins or fibres mark out in the leaves of nearly all trees.

Malpighi Discerns the Proof of the Circulation

Marcello Malpighi (1628–94) is regarded as one of the great microscopists of his time, having pioneered in the study of the embryology of the chick, the complex anatomy of the silkworm, the anatomy of the tracheal systems of insects, and above all the histology of most organs of the mammalian body, including the newly discovered lymph glands. Besides being one of the founders of modern histology, he published many investigations on the anatomy of plants and on gall flies and galls; he was the first to see that the latter organisms served as homes for grubs.

In these two letters to his friend Borelli, Malpighi reports his detection of two separate systems of interconnecting vessels and vesicles, the air and blood networks of the lung. His style is neither lucid nor dramatic, and he does not seem too excited over his discovery, as some pioneers are wont to be. This may be due in part to the fact that the presence of air in the lungs and of anastomoses of veins and arteries in tissues had been thought of for so long and so persistently that he took it for granted that they should be there. But Malpighi is no superficial student of the wonders of nature. He pursues the subject quite thoroughly even in his wordy and meandering Epistle I, and by the time he dispatches the second one, he is quite clear on what he has stumbled across. He blows air into the lungs and notes that the pulmonary artery stands out "like a sculpture in relief," with "its extending vesicles in the form of branches of a tree." He injects mercury into a blood vessel but reaches no specific conclusion about the fusion of the arterial and venous streams. "This question thus far troubles my mind," he says. He injects colored fluids into the pulmonary artery and sees them enter the veins but also "ooze through the investing membrane . . . accumulate in the interstices" and spurt out through the trachea. The relevant and accidental phenomena are thus interlinked in his mind and in his report, and not knowing which is which, he throws up his hands in dismay, saying that, injections being unnatural, a variety of things can happen. He does suggest, however, that the lungs maintain the proper mixing of the blood's white and red components and speculates on blood formation through fermentation.

In his Epistle II, Malpighi is sure of the union of the two blood streams in the lung. The incoming venous blood "flows away through the tortuous vessels." His demonstration of tying the lung to watch with a microscope the flow of the blood in the lung's capillaries is the first recorded experiment of its kind. The next excerpt will put this fundamental bit of evidence for the correctness of Harvey's theory on its firmest foundation.

12. ANTONY VAN LEEUWENHOEK

On the Circulation of the Blood

When these tadpoles were about eight or ten days old, I could perceive a small particle moving within their bodies, which I concluded to be the heart; and the fluid which was protruded from it began to assume a red colour.

Upon examing the tail of this creature, a sight presented itself, more delightful than any that my eyes had ever beheld; for here I discovered more than fifty circulations of the blood, in different places, while the animal lay quiet in the water, and I could bring it before the miscroscope to my wish. For I saw, not only that the blood in many places was conveyed through exceedingly minute vessels, from the middle of the tail toward the edges, but that each of these vessels had a curve, or turning, and carried the blood back towards the middle of the tail, in order to be again conveyed to the heart. Hereby it plainly appeared to me, that the blood-vessels I now saw in this animal, and which bear the names of arteries and veins, are, in fact, one and the same, that is to say, that they are properly termed

From *The Select Works of Antony van Leeuwenhoek (1632–1723), Containing His Microscopical Discoveries in Many of the Works of Nature,* translated by S. Hoole, H. Fry, London, 1798, pp. 89–112 and 322–5.

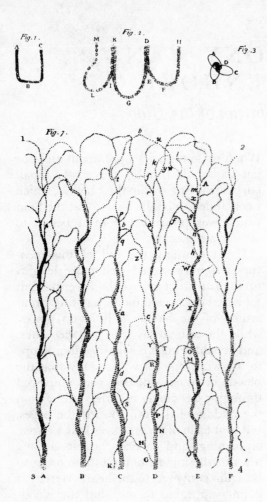

Plate IV.

arteries so long as they convey the blood to the farthest extremities of its vessels, and veins when they bring it back towards the heart. For example, I see many blood-vessels in the tail of a tadpole taking their course, as represented in Plate IV. fig. 1. A B C, where the position of the parts A and C is towards the spine or middle of the tail, and the part B towards the edge of it. In A B, the blood is driven from the heart, and in B C, it is brought back again, and thus may we say, that the vessel A B C, is both an artery and a vein; for it cannot be denominated an artery, farther than where the blood is driven in it to its farthest extent, that is, from A to B; and we must name B C, a vein, because, in it, the blood is returning back to the heart. And thus it appears, that an artery and a vein are one and the same vessel prolonged or extended.

In the part where I saw this circulation, the arteries were no larger than to admit a single particle of blood to pass freely through them: these particles, though in this creature they were of a flat and oval shape, yet sometimes by reason of the smallness of the artery, assumed a kind of oblong round figure, and when the animal, by being taken out of the water, grew languid, the blood in these very minute arteries began to stagnate, and when it again acquired motion, many of the globules appeared twice as long as broad, and also pointed at their extremities.

In another place, I saw a larger artery divide itself into two branches, which are shown at fig. 2. D E, and each of these branches returned back with a curve, as represented at E F and E G. Now, if we denominate D E F, and D E G, arteries, because, in them the blood is driven outwards from the heart, it follows that F H, and G I K, must be veins, because they each bring it back toward the heart. Again, not far from K, was another smaller artery, which is figured at M L; this was united to the vein I K, so that the arteries D E G, and M L, together formed one vein at I K. In a word, in this figure, H F is a vein, D E F and D E G, are arteries; G I K and K I L, are veins, and M L is an artery; and yet we must say, that these are only the same vessels continued.

In another place I saw three of the smallest arteries, after returning in a curve, as before described, unite in one, and thus form a vein three times the size of each artery. But all three vessels with their bendings wherein the circulation was performed did not occupy more space, than could be covered by a grain of sand. . . .

But, as I became then well assured, that this conjunction,

or circulation, did not take place in the larger vessels, but in the very smallest of all, (for otherwise I am persuaded, that all the parts of the body could not be supplied with nourishment) and that therefore I should in vain attempt to discover such circulation, I some years ago, abandoned the farther investigation of it. For, if we now plainly perceive, that the passage of the blood from the arteries into the veins of the tadpole, is not performed in any other than those vessels, which are so minute as only to admit the passage of a single globule at a time, we may conclude that the same is performed in like manner in our own bodies, and in those of other animals. ...

The particles in the blood of frogs are (as before observed) of a flat and oval shape, and these, when viewed singly, appear, as I may say, colourless; but when two are laid on one another, they appear a little of a reddish cast; and where three are together, the redness becomes deeper. This may be explained by fig. 3 wherein A represents one of these oval particles, which, in part, is covered by another particle B; and C is a third particle, covering a small part of both A and B; by which means the part at D, where the particles are threefold, acquires a still darker colour.

• • • • • •

In Plate IV. fig. 7, and in the space between 1, 2, 3, 4, are represented six of these blood-vessels, which I directed to be drawn on rather a larger scale than the first sketch taken of them, in order that the several vessels might be easier distinguished; therefore this figure shews them about twice as large as they appeared to the limner through the microscope.

These vessels were not at the very extremity of the fish's tail, but a little below it, towards the end of the fin. And that part, or spot, which the limner saw through the microscope, and the several blood-vessels of which he made the drawing, did not, in my judgment, take up as much space as is occupied by a large grain of sand; for though the view of the microscope might include the compass of four such grains, yet the part wherein the blood-vessels were seen, did not amount to a fourth of that space; so that, within less compass than that of a grain of sand, there are found to be in the tail of an eel, as great a number of blood-vessels as are here represented between 1, 2, 3, 4.

At the letter A, is represented one of those blood-vessels, which are called veins; B, one of those named arteries; C, is a vein; D, an artery; E, another vein, and F, another artery.

But, in order more clearly to explain the course of the blood in these vessels, and to shew, at what part, though in fact they are one and the same, they assume different names, I have in the figure more particularly pointed out, and shall now describe one of those vessels called an artery.

D, is that artery, out of which, at G, proceeds a finall branch, which, at H, divides itself into two, as H I K; and here we see, that the branch G H I is properly to be named an artery, because, as far as I, the blood is driven from the heart, and I K, we must name a vein, because, from I to K the blood is brought back towards the heart. In the other branch, which proceeds from H, in the direction H L M, the blood is infused into the vein E at M; and since at M it first begins to take its course towards the heart, it follows that at M the vessel first assumes the name of a vein.

. . . . .

I then took an eel about a foot long and placed it before the microscope, and, from the most correct observation which I could make, I judged that in the seventy-second part of a minute, the blood in one of the arteries, which was of a size to admit three or four globules of blood at a time to pass through it, had proceeded the space of a fifteenth part of an inch; therefore the blood, in one minute's time, passed over a space of four inches and four-fifths of an inch; and this number being multiplied by sixty minutes, it follows that the blood in this eel could be carried or driven forward 288 inches in the space of an hour.

Now, let us suppose that the heart (which in eels is placed near the head) was in this eel distant from the end of the tail, where the farthest extent of the circulation is performed, 11 inches, it follows that the blood, in its circulation, must be carried twice this distance, being 22 inches, before it returned back to the heart; and dividing the above mentioned number, 288 by 22, we shall find that in this eel the blood circulated to the extremity of the tail and back to the heart, something more than thirteen times in the space of an hour.

In the next place, we will suppose that the ends of the blood-vessels in the head, and in the fins next to the head, were in this eel one inch and an half distant from the heart, and consequently, that in these vessels the blood only performed a circuit of three inches; it will follow, by the same mode of computation as before, that in these parts the blood might perform its circulation ninety-six times in the space of an hour.

Leeuwenhoek's "Trifling Observations"

With Malpighi and Leeuwenhoek a new vital technique entered the field of biological research, the use of the microscope. Although the application of lenses affected almost every science, the most dramatic impact was in astronomy and biology.

Glass had been known since remotest ancient times, and the Greco-Roman world had been acqainted with magnification by lenses and mirrors, even though reading glasses, to be worn on the nose, did not gain common acceptance until about 1300 A.D. In spite of the prevalence of lenses, three centuries passed before someone thought of putting two convex lenses together to provide increased magnification and overcome distance. It was in 1610 that Galileo, after hearing of the invention of a telescope in Holland and of its use in the discernment of distant objects on sea or land, designed one for himself, combining a planoconvex objective lens with a plano-concave eyepiece. He aimed it, with an uncanny sense of the significant, at the high spots of the celestial scene and soon reported to a stunned world his amazing findings. His book *The Starry Messenger,* issued in 1610, became something of a best seller. In it he writes,* "About ten months ago a report reached my ears that a certain Fleming had constructed a spyglass by means of which visible objects, though very distant from the eye of the observer, were distinctly seen as if nearby. Of this truly remarkable effect several experiences were related, to which some persons gave credence while others denied them." Galileo also constructed a microscope, although he was not the first to do this, either. Although he revolutionized astronomy with his telescope in only a few months, he never exploited the microscope. Apparently the area in which it could be utilized held no interest for him. There were, however, numerous naturalists who were lured by the unknown microscopic world even as Galileo and Kepler were by the wonders of the starry firmament. From the mid-seventeenth century to the beginning of the eighteenth century, several keen and brilliant investigators who

---

* S. Drake, *Discoveries and Opinions of Galileo,* Doubleday, Garden City, N.Y., 1957, p. 28.

worked chiefly as microscopists appeared, with Malpighi and Leeuwenhoek conspicuous among them.

Antony van Leeuwenhoek (1632–1723) was one of the greatest scientific explorers of all time. He was neither professor nor physician but one of a new breed of self-trained amateurs who as a group made significant contributions to the burgeoning sciences. A draper by trade, he lived all his humble life in the city of Delft, Holland, devoting all his free time to the building of simple, that is, single-lensed, microscopes of remarkable precision and resolution, employing them in the study of literally everything he could lay his hands upon. In the course of his unquenchable searches for the normally unseen, he discovered protozoa, bacteria, sperm cells, red blood cells, capillaries, plant and animal tissues and organs, crystal structures, and hundreds of other biological and physical novelties. He described accurately the anatomies of many insects and the life cycles of aphids, ants, and a host of parasite forms, and he clarified the germination of seeds, thus opening up vast areas for further study. In his later life he gained worldwide renown. His works have come down to us in the form of letters to the secretary of the Royal Society of London, beginning with the summer of 1673.

Leeuwenhoek's observations are invariably those of a master. His speculations are often naive, but on occasion they are most perspicacious. For example, he reasons that since the large arteries are thick-walled, they obviously cannot be the sites of delivery of nourishment to the tissues. Rather must "the particles of blood from which its redness proceeds" deliver their "more subtile juices" through the capillary walls, "whereby the blood, when returning in the veins, being deprived of those juices which are taken away, it will appear blackish." He devotes much space to showing that a blood clot caused by a blow is not removed by perspiration. The blood stream bypasses a clot when possible. When an artery is blocked by one, then with each heartbeat blood surges forward but is sent back by the clot, thus forming "a swift alternate or reciprocal motion, like that of a saw." In such uncomplicated ways he establishes a visual proof of the meaning of the pulse, a problem upon which Galen pondered in so many volumes and which Harvey resolved as a segment of his visionary scheme. He does it with the same charmingly simple, disarmingly direct, and logically incontrovertible technique with which, in the passage here cited, he proves the actual continuity of the flow of the blood cells and blood plasma from arterioles directed away from the heart, into capillaries, and next into venules and veins directed toward the heart. What Harvey was obliged to postulate on the basis of his theory, Leeuwenhoek demonstrates in his sincere but irrefutable manner with the aid of his homemade microscope, his extraordinary skill, and his gift of experimental ingenuity.

He is equally ingenious in determining the volumes of clots and the speed of the blood stream. He seems to enjoy measuring and calculating and employs these devices whenever possible. Since one red cell traverses $\frac{1}{15}$ of an inch in $\frac{1}{72}$ of a minute, it must travel $\frac{1}{15} \times 72 = 4.8$ inches per minute, or $4.8 \times 60 = 288$ inches per hour. Since the eel is 11 inches long, the blood flows back and forth $11 + 11 = 22$ inches, making that trip a little over 13 times per hour, or $\frac{288}{22}$. He applies the same method to man with fairly reasonable results, in view of the numerous factors involved of which he could not possibly be aware. All in all, his and Malpighi's discoveries constitute a triumph for Harvey's theory and offer clearcut proof of the very foundation Harvey built upon.

Only rarely does Leeuwenhoek's speculation lead him astray. Thus he examines the wing of a grasshopper and errs through reasoning by analogy. He takes the tubes in the insect's wing and their branching tubules for blood vessels because of their great similarity in appearance to them and fancies that he sees "globules swimming in the clear liquor" contained in them. When these globules are gathered in heaps, they show "a lively green." It so happens that insects have some kind of bloodlike fluid within their bodies but not one that circulates in vessels and capillaries. Their network of tubules circulates air throughout their bodies, which are thick, as Leeuwenhoek correctly noted. The vessels that he saw in the insect's wing were air tubules, which feed the living wing tissue and carry no fluid. He detailed carefully what he observed, and his misinterpretation did no harm, for he called attention to an important structure that future study was bound to place in its proper context.

13. PHILOSOPHICAL TRANSACTIONS

An Account of more Tryals of Transfusion, accompanied with some Considerations thereon

chiefly in reference to its circumspect Practise on Man; together with a farther Vindication of this Invention from Usurpers.

This Experiment, as it hath raised Disputes among the *Curious* both here and abroad; so it hath put some of them upon considering such ways, and given such cautions, as many render the use of it safe and beneficial. Of the number of these seems to be that *French* Virtuoso, *Gasper de Gurye de Montpoly,* who in a late *Letter* of his to Monsieur *Bourdelot,* declares to the World, that this is a very Ingenious Invention, and such an one, as may prove very useful; but withall, that, in his opinion, it is to be used with much caution, as not being like to be practised innoxiously, if imprudent men do mannage it, and the concourse of two differing sorts of Blood requiring many tryals, and a careful observation of many circumstances, to give assurance. He supposes, that the Blood of every Animal is endowed with its peculiar Temper, and contains in the Aggregate of its parts, different natures, principles, fig-

From *Philosophical Transactions of the Royal Society of London,* **2,** 517 (1667).

ures, and even a different Center. Whence he concludes, that two Substances thus differing, and containing plenty of spirits, are not reducible to one and the same Center, nor to one and the same Body without *Fermentation;* and that this Operation may prove of danger to him, that shall have admitted into his Veins a strange Blood (wont to be free in its native Vessels) without passing through those degrees that must give it Impressions sutable to the temper and functions of the Vitals of the *Recipient:* And taking for granted, that no considerate man will hazard a *Total* Transfusion, he acknowledges that a *Partial* one may be in some cases and sicknesses very useful, provided, it be practised circumspectly, upon a Body yet strong enough, and in a *moderate* quantity, so as the Spirits and Blood of the *Recipient* may be able to dissolve and master the transfused strange Blood, and convert the same into its own nature by a gentle *Ebullition;* to obtain by such a commixture a principle of motion, that may cause a better habit of Body. And he believes, that this Ebullition must always happen in Bloods of differing parts and qualities; and that very hardly two Animals, of differing species, ages and tempers, will be met with, that have Blood so like one another, as not to need *Fermentation,* to make a requisit mixture. He doubts not, that if a substance could be found so resembling that of our Spirits, as that it would immediately unite it self with them, not needing any alteration, the Transfusion of such a Substance would be capable to produce effects little less than miraculous, by relieving the prostrated forces of Nature, and by fortifying in us the Spring of the motion and life: In a word, by exciting that Principle of continual Motion, which, whilst it has strength enough, still subdues and gathers to it self whatever is proper to entertain it, and rejects what is not so. But such an Invention as this he sees cause to esteem very difficult, in regard that *different* Moulds cannot but characterize things *differently.* Hence he proceeds to the Examples, wherein *Transfusion* hath been experimented, even upon *Men;* alledged in that known ingenious Letter of Monsieur *Denys.* And here he intimates, how much he was pleased to learn, that, according to his Conjecture, a

Blood transfusion from animal to man. (From Purmann's book on military surgery, 1721.)

Moderate Intromission of Blood hath well succeeded, and the *Fermentation,* which we foresaw would be caused by the commixture of two Bloods, was made with advantage to the Patient: Which he judges did manifestly appear by his Bleeding at the Nose, (a sign of an *Ebullition* made in the Blood:) confirmed to him by this, that an expert Acquaintance of his, transfusing a great quantity of Blood into several Doggs, observed always, that the *Receiving* Doggs pissed Blood.

And as to the other successful Experiment, made upon a healthy and robust man, he notes, that he being a lusty Fellow, stored with blood, and taking the Air, and working hard on the same day that the tryal was made upon him, his vigorous Blood, Spirits, and Constitution, and the strong motion of his Heart, were able to convert into the substance of his own Blood that of the *Lamb* received, and to impart thereto his own nature, and to mould it into Figures sutable to the pores where it was to pass, and proper to the functions it was to perform.

But to these Reflections he subjoyns two other *Instances,* of an unlike success; whereof the one is afforded by a *Man,* the other by a *Dogg.* As to the *Man,* it ought to be related beforehand, to prevent wonder or misconstruction, that his Intestines, when he was opened after death, were found to be gangren'd, and consequently, that then he appeared to have been a subject altogether unfit for this Experiment, seeing it was naturally impossible for him to live with such a putrefaction. But to come to the tryal it self; this *Author* saith, that Baron *Bond,* Son to the first Minister of State to the King of *Sweeden,* undergoing the Operation twice, appeared the first time to find new strength by it; but expired soon after the second Operation: The Ebullition, it seems, of the corrupt Blood having mastered and enervated all the Blood he had in his Body; which, when open'd no Blood at all was found in his Heart: probably, as the *Author* conjectureth, upon this account, that there being not left in the *Patient* Blood enough of his own, nor strength sufficient to turn a strange Blood into a substance homogenius to *that;* the Heart was not capable to admit the Blood of the *Emittent,* as consisting of parts dispro-portionate to his own. But, as hath been already observed, his Entrails were altogether vitiated by a *Gangrene,* and he therefore out of the reach of being relieved by this Experiment.

Concerning the other *Instance, viz.* of the *Doggs,* the *Letter* affirms, that the Tryal was made by Monsieur *Gayen* with great exactness, after this manner. He drew three great dishes of Blood from the Dog that was to receive, and weighed the other Dog that was to furnish; and the operation being perform'd, he weighed him again, and found him weigh less than he did by *two* pounds; of which having abated an *ounce* more or less, for the Urine, made by the Dog, and an *ounce* or *two* more for the Blood spilt in the operation, there remaineth at least *one* pound and a *half* of Blood, that was transfused. But, the *Recipient,* though well dress'd, and well fed, died *five* days after, the *Emittent* being yet alive. Whence it seems evident to this *Writer,* that the *too large* Intromission of *new* Blood was predominant over the *Native,* and as 'twere, over-whelm'd it. Whence he again inculcates the dangerousness of infusing *too much* Blood at once, in regard that such Blood being now separated from the principle of life it had in the *Emittent,* and as yet destitute of the stamp necessary to live the life of the *Recipient,* it could not be moved and assimilated by the live Blood, which remained in the *Recipient;* and the *Fermentation,* that was made, passed rather to an Eagerness or Sowerness, than to such an one as precedes Digestion. And this kind of eager acidity *he intimates* was seen by the Spectators, and felt by the Receiving Animal, which swounded, and remained as dead for half a quarter of an hour: And when some alledged, that the Dog died, because he was wounded in the neck, where he could not lick himself, which rendred his wound incureable, answer was given, that Experiments had been made, wherein not only a Vein was opened, but also an Artery, yea, even the *Aspera arteria* cut of a Dog, that could not lick himself, and yet survived.

This whole Account is concluded with an Admonition, that all those, who have conveniency, would make frequent and exact trials of this Experiment on *Brutes,* and carefully observe *Weight* and *Measure,* and all other circumstances, before any thing be hazarded, that may damnify the publick, and depreciate the invention.

Abundans cautela non nocet, is a Maxime very fit to be minded here; though several succesful Experiments have been made in *London,* of very plentiful Transfusions; and among others (to mention a signal one) that upon a *Bitch,* which lost in the operation near 30 ounces of blood, and was recruited accordingly. This Animal does not only survive to this very day, but had another more severe Experiment soon after tryed upon her, by which her *Spleen* was cut out, without tying up the Vessels, whence that *viscus* was separated: Since which time (even before the wound was healed up) she took dog, was with Puppy, and brought forth Whelps, and remains well and jocund, being kept for a piece of remarquable Curiosity in the House of a Noble-man, that is as severe in Examining matters of fact, as He is able in Judging of their consequences.

So that it is not too hastily to be concluded, that *large* Transfusions are dangerous; but rather frequent Experiments should be made, before any thing be therein determined, with great as well as smaller quantities, both upon sound and sickly Beasts, carefully observing, how either is endured in either, and what are the Effects following thereon.

Before we dismiss this *Subject,* something is to be said of the Cause, why the Curious in *England* make a demurr in practising this Experiment upon *Men.* The above-mentioned ingenious Monsieur *Denys* has acquainted the World, how this degree was ventured upon at *Paris,* and what good success it there met with: And the *Journal des Scavans* glorieth, that the *French* have advanced this Invention so far, as to try it upon *Men,* before any *English* did it, and that with good success.

We readily grant, *They* were the first, we know off, that actually thus *improved* the Experiment; but then they must give us leave to inform them of this Truth, that the Philosophers in *England* had practised it long ago upon *Man,* if they had not been so tender in hazarding the Life of Man (which they take so much pain, to preserve and relieve) nor so scrupulous to incur the Penalties of the Law, which in *England,* is more strict and nice in cases of this concernment, than those of many other Nations are.

The *Publisher* can assert *bonâ fide,* that several Moneths agoe he saw himself the *Instruments* ready, and heard the *Method* agreed on, thought proper to execute this Operation upon Man. And, for further proof thereof, he shall here insert the whole way, peculiarly contrived here for this purpose, by the ingenious Dr. *Edmund King,* and by him communicated in a Letter; Monsieur *Denys* not having thought fit to describe the *manner* they used in *France* for *Men;* nor any body else come to our knowledge.

Early Transfusions and a Warning

In the seventh issue of the first volume of the Philosophical Transactions of the Royal Society of London, which began publication on March 6, 1664/5, there appeared a brief article written by the editor and entitled "An Account of the Rise and Attempts of a Way to convey Liquors immediately into the Mass of Blood." The essence of the article is in fact given in the introductory sentence. "Whereas there have lately appeared in publick some Books, printed beyond the Seas, treating of the way of Injecting Liquors into Veins; in which Books the Original of that Invention seems to be ascribed to others, besides him, to whom it really belongs; It will surely not be thought amiss, if something be said whereby the true Inventor's right may beyond exception be asserted and preserved, To which end, there will need no more than barely to represent the Time when, and the place where, and among whom it was first started and put to tryal." The man who was the first to make an injection of opium and an infusion of Crocus Metallorum was "the learned and ingenious Dr. Christopher Wren," assisted by Robert Boyle. The injected animal was a dog. A foreign ambassador living in London, probably French, tried it next on a criminal, "with this success, that the Fellow, as soon as ever the Injection began to be made, did, either really or craftily fall into a swoon, whereby, being unwilling to prosecute so hazardous an Experiment, they desisted."

A year and a half later there appeared in the same journal an item of six lines announcing that Dr. Lower had transfused blood from one animal into another and describing the feat as "This experiment, hitherto look'd upon to be of an almost unsurmountable difficulty." It was carried out at the request of Robert Boyle and stimulated the editor to enumerate sixteen questions. Will such transfusions change a fierce dog into a coward? Will a dog possessing new blood remember his master? Will the recipient gain the qualities of the donor or lose those he had acquired or possessed? Will a hungry recipient be fed by the chyle of another? Will his fur or color change? Can recipients accept blood from other species? And so on. The transfusions were made through tubes connecting the blood systems of the two animals.

Later papers described transfusions between calves and sheep. The first step was to remove blood from the veins of the recipient sheep, which became weak as a result. Its jugular vein was then joined by a tube to the jugular vein of a donor calf. Both animals were subsequently bled to death. One experiment was recorded in which a mangy dog was allowed to give blood to a normal one, jugular to jugular; the sick donor was cured within two weeks, and the sound recipient showed no sign of the disease. Finally, in the June 1667 issue there was a report from France that blood was transfused from a young dog into the veins of an old one, bringing about the latter's rejuvenation. The paper reproduced here follows in time the appearance of this last one.

Several transfusions had been performed on human patients in both France and Italy. At first, great claims were made for the wonderful therapeutic effects of such heroic treatment. However, after only a few years of claims and counterclaims and the deaths of several victims, there arose such a public uproar in France that all experimentation along these lines was abandoned, not to be resumed until the twentieth century.

What is significant about the excerpt presented here is the appeal to caution in transfusions by Gasper de Gurye de Montpoly on the basis of few experiments, some of which had even been considered successful. In the light of future developments, it must be remarked that this passage contains some valuable and farsighted thoughts. Founded though they were on little evidence, and speculative though they were in nature, resting upon assumptions of fermentation and ebullition, which had the vaguest definitions and the loosest applications, the ideas struck, nevertheless, directly at the core of the problem and could only serve to guide future research along profitable lines. They did not lead to immediate results because the practical tools and concepts needed for their implementation were entirely lacking; moreover, when these became available, the acumen demonstrated here seemed to be neither remembered nor utilized. Yet the fact remains that de Montpoly's conclusions anticipated the discovery of blood groups, antibodies, and compatible transfusability. The historian of science finds it of utmost interest that de Montpoly based his judgments not on what is frequently designated as "the scientific method" or "scientific logic" but rather on insight. Insights are always stimulating and creative. They resemble the mutations that feed the process of natural selection. If it were not for their diversity, there would be no evolution.

14. ROBERT HOOKE

An Account of an Experiment made by Mr. Hook

[OF PRESERVING ANIMALS ALIVE BY BLOWING
THROUGH THEIR LUNGS WITH BELLOWS.]

This Noble Experiment came not to the Publisher's *hands, till all the preceding Particulars
were already sent to the Press, and almost all
Printed off, (for which cause also it could not be
mentioned among the* Contents: *(And it might
have been reserved for the next opportunity, had
not the considerableness thereof been a motive to
hasten its Publication. It shall be here annexed
in the Ingenious* Author *his own words, as he
presented it to the* Royal Society, October.
24. 1667. *the Experiment it self having been
both* repeated *(after a former successful trial of
it, made by the same hand a good while agoe)*
and *improved the week before, at their* publick
Assembly. *The Relation it self follows;*

I did heretofore give this *Illustrious Society* an account of an Experiment I formerly tryed of keeping a Dog alive after
his *Thorax* was all display'd by the cutting
away of the *Ribs* and *Diaphragme;* and after
the *Pericardium* of the Heart also was taken
off. But divers persons seeming to doubt of
the certainty of the Experiment (by reason
that some Tryals of this matter, made by

From *Philosophical Transactions of the Royal Society of
London*, **2,** 539 (1667).

other hands, failed of success) I caus'd at the last Meeting the same Experiment to be shewn in the presence of this *Noble Company,* and that with the same success, as it had been made by me at first; the Dog being kept alive by the Reciprocal blowing up of his Lungs with *Bellowes,* and they suffered to subside, for the space of an hour or more, after his *Thorax* had been so display'd, and his *Aspera arteria* cut off just below the *Epigolotis* and bound on upon the nose of the Bellows.

And because some Eminent Physicians had affirm'd, that the *Motion of the Lungs* was necessary to Life upon the account of promoting the Circulation of the Blood, and that it was conceiv'd, the Animal would immediately be suffocated as soon as the Lungs should cease to be moved, I did (the better to fortifie my own *Hypothesis* of this matter, and to be the better able to Judge of several others) make the following additional Experiment; *viz.*

The Dog having been kept alive, (as I have now mentioned) for above an hour, in which time the Tryal hath often been repeated, in suffering the dog to fall into *Convulsive* motions by ceasing to blow the Bellows, and permitting the Lungs to subside and lye still, and of suddenly reviving him again by renewing the blast, and consequently the motion of the Lungs: This I say, having been done, and the Judicious Spectators fully satisfied of the reality of the former Experiment; I caused another pair of Bellows to be immediately joyn'd to the first, by a contrivance, I had prepar'd, and pricking all the outercoat of the Lungs with the slender point of a very sharp pen-knive, this second pair of Bellows was mov'd very quick, whereby the first pair was always kept full and always blowing into the Lungs; by which means the Lungs also were always kept very full, and without any motion, there being a continual blast of Air forc'd into the Lungs by the first pair of Bellows, supplying it as fast, as it could find its way quite through the Coat of the Lungs by the small holes pricked in it, as was said before. This being continued for a pretty while, the dog, as I expected, lay still, as before, his eyes being all the time very quick, and his Heart beating very regularly: But, upon ceasing this blast, and suffering the Lungs to fall and lye still, the Dog would immediately fall into Dying convulsive fits; but be as soon reviv'd again by the renewing the fulness of his Lungs with the constant blast of fresh Air.

Towards the latter end of this Experiment a piece of the Lungs was cut quite off; where 'twas observable, that the Blood did freely circulate, and pass thorow the Lungs, not only when the Lungs were kept thus constantly extended, but also when they were suffered to subside and ly still. Which seem to be Arguments, that as the *bare* Motion of the Lungs *without fresh* Air contributes nothing to the life of the Animal, he being found to survive as well when they were not mov'd, as when they were; so it was not the subsiding or movelesness of the Lungs that was the immediate cause of Death, or the stopping the Circulation of the Blood through the Lungs, but the *want* of a sufficient *supply of fresh Air*.

I shall shortly further try, whether the suffering the Blood to circulate through a vessel, so as it may be openly exposed to the fresh Air, will not suffice for the life of an Animal; and make some other Experiments, which, I hope, will throughly discover the *Genuine use of Respiration;* and afterwards consider of what benefit this may be to Mandkind.

A Model Experiment by Hooke

This experiment by the "universally curious" Robert Hooke (1635–1703) is to the point and unequivocal. One might almost say that it is the ideal or model experiment with which to illustrate discussions on the so-called scientific method, as presented in textbooks and essays on the philosophy of science. Hooke asks a few simple questions and performs skillful experiments to answer them. He arrests the natural motion of the lungs and effects artificially their alternate inflation and collapse, in simulation of their natural motion. The dog's heart continues to beat, and the animal is kept alive for some time.

He also finds an answer to the question: "Is the motion of the lungs, as such, required for the maintenance of life?" Many of his contemporaries believed that it was. Hooke shows that cessation of lung motion throws the dog into convulsions and that restoration of the air blast revives him. But he then goes on to demonstrate that it is the fresh air, not the lung motion, that maintains life.

It is probably not a coincidence that this kind of experiment was performed by a man like Hooke, who was ingenious, mechanically minded, inventive, clever with instruments, and possessed of the broadest scientific interests. The very fact that he was in turn assistant to Christopher Wren, Robert Boyle, and Isaac Newton is sufficient to establish his greatness, as well as his shortcomings. For forty years he was Curator of Experiments to the newly founded Royal Society and "the pivot of its scientific work." As a rule, if the problem was one requiring a simple attack or a novel device, without sustained speculation of either general abstractness or mathematical complexity, Hooke was certain to find some solution. His technical inventiveness and experimental common sense never fail to amaze. His diary, in which are recorded the ideas and experiments that filled his active, if not too happy, years, covers the whole spectrum of scientific thought of his day, and few are the subjects to which he did not make some contribution, however small. As Sir William Petty put it, his was indeed a mind of "tumultuous versatility." His discoveries and inventions ranged over plant and animal tissues and organs (he introduced the term *cell*), microscopes, telescopes, barometers, air pumps, clocks, the action of a spring, the nature of winds, currents, comets, meteors, earthquakes, rocks, minerals, crystals, and metals, surveying, architecture, navigation, etc. His curiosity was endless, and his skill direct and poignant. He was never diverted by theoretical considerations or driven by intense concentration along a single line of research. His mode of approach may have had limitations, but it certainly could boast many compensations, as the work cited here attests.

15. RICHARD LOWER

Treatise on the Heart

[TRACTATUS DE CORDE]

Finally, the movement of the Heart is shown to be independent of any ebullition of blood by the fact that a Heart taken from a living animal and entirely emptied of blood does not cease to move, even if it is cut into small pieces. It is a matter of common knowledge that the Hearts of fairly young animals, long after they have been cut out of the thorax, pick up their pulsations at once, and continue them for a long time, if they are gently stimulated with a small pin. Eels' Hearts, similarly stimulated with a needle several hours after they have been taken out, are seen to pulsate once more, since their spirits are entrapped and entangled in the rather viscous matter and are unable to escape so quickly.

But, to decide experimentally whether or not any ebullition of blood helped the blood's movement at all, it occurred to me to see if the Heart would continue its movement undiminished, after I had drawn off the blood, and had replaced it

From *Early Science in Oxford,* edited by R. T. Gunther, Oxford University Press, London, 1932, Volume IX, Chapter III (On the Movement and Colour of the Blood), pp. 152–71, and Chapter V (On the Passage of the Chyle into the Blood), pp. 193–200.

intravenously by an equal quantity of other fluids, less liable to become lighter or to froth up. With this object in mind I drew off through the jugular vein of a Dog almost half its total blood volume, injecting instead through the crural vein an equal amount of beer mixed with a little wine. This procedure I repeated several times in succession until, instead of blood, the fluid coming from the vein was merely a solution with less colour than the washings of meat, or than claret several times diluted. The Heartbeat, meanwhile, became only slowly more feeble, so that practically the whole of the blood was replaced by beer before life was replaced by death.

 . . . . .

I am so far from believing the movement of the blood to be dependent on any heating of it within the Heart, that I do not think it owes any of its heat to this organ. Although the Heart should, rightly enough, be acknowledged as the source of heat (and heat is carried from it to all parts of the body), it will not perhaps be any truer to say that heat is produced only in this organ, or that the blood is warmed only by it, than that the waters of hot springs receive their heat from the bath into which they discharge, and not from the intrinsic fire of the parts which they bathe and wash against in their passage in the bowels of the earth. For there is nothing in the Heart which is sufficient to produce so much heat. It is certain, in any case, that the Heart does not produce its own heat, but needs to be warmed just as it is nourished entirely by the blood flowing into it from the arteries.

. . . For, while the blood is cooled in the extremities, where it is exposed, practically without covering, to the external air during its passage, it is equally certain that it warms up as soon as it enters the enclosed cavities of the thorax and the abdomen. It is thus that fat, well-covered men, whose blood-vessels lie more deeply and are buried in flesh, are better able to withstand cold than thin men, although the Hearts of such excessively fat men are not so active and strong as are those of men, who are more slender and thinner.

 . . . . .

I should here speak of the ultimate way in which the heart's movement is effected, but, as it is over-difficult to obtain any due conception of this, and it is the privilege of God alone, who comprehends the heart's secrets, to understand its movement also, I will not waste effort in examining it further.

It will suffice, therefore, if I merely observe that the force and strength, by which the heart expels with regular, even beat the blood that falls continuously into its chambers, do not arise from anything within the heart, but come down into it from the head above, as if from heaven. The heart is, functionally, extremely important and necessary, and nature therefore exerts such care and solicitude in the execution of its movement, that, in addition to the important nerve-branches distributed thickly all over it, she has also prepared the cerebellum as a perpetual storeroom of animal spirits, so that there may be a continuous inflow of them into the heart. This organ is so dependent on their liberal and continuous inflow that, if this is cut off for even the smallest period of time, the heart's movement ceases there and then. If the nerves of the eighth pair are tightly ligatured in the neck, or are divided (which is much the same thing as far as the animal is concerned) it is remarkable how great a change suddenly occurs! The heart, which before beat quickly and regularly, begins to palpitate and quiver as soon as the ligature is applied; the wretched animal prolongs a weary life for a day or two to the accompaniment of heart-tremor and excessive dyspnoea, and finally dies without warning.

The degree of cardiac distress which the animal soon feels as a result of such section or ligature is well shown by the rapid onset of convulsive movements, which are so pronounced and violent that it is difficult, without using strong cords, to keep the animal in the same place or position of the body.

· · · · · ·

But while it is true that the movement of the blood and of the heart depends entirely on the brain, as seen above, yet, so that such great advantages should not be thought to be freely conferred on one of them only, it will not be amiss to note in passing that, although the brain is master over all the organs of the body below it, as a king over his subjects, and rules and governs all at its will and command, it is not so placed above them that it can survive or have any power in the absence of their help and service. On the contrary, the animal spirits, and life itself, are so dependent on the continuous supply of blood to the brain, that every kind of suppression of this supply soon leads to syncope and unconsciousness, and further, if such processes persist unduly long, the life of the animal ceases completely. The reason for this is simply that the animal spirits, through the constant inflow of blood, trickle down the nerves from the brain to provide for the continuation of the movement of the chest and of the heart, and must therefore be replenished by a constant supply of blood. So the brain, if deprived of its right and continuous distribution of this fluid, suffers a sort of eclipse, and the animal, robbed of sensation and movement, falls of its own weight; as one can see in those attacked by syncope.

. . . . .

The trunks of the arteries, then, are endowed with a thicker and stronger coat, and so they are kept everywhere within their proper limit, when there is equally open access for the blood to all organs. When, however, their lumen is blocked and closed by some impacted matter, or they are obliterated and dried up by the wasting of the parts, or the channel of any particular one is compressed and constricted by any external body or circumstance, then, as the amount of blood is proportioned to the body as a whole, and the force imparted to it by the heart is constant, whenever the blood's passage is hindered in any one artery, those arteries nearest to it and in association with it must sustain the rush of the expelled blood, and themselves take up the whole amount destined for this other artery. Hence it sometimes happens that, when the lumen of some artery has been too long obstructed or ligated, the blood busies itself in opening a wider channel for its passage in the neighbouring artery; and, until this happens, the movement of the blood in all the arteries around must of necessity be greatly accelerated and conducted with greater haste. The blood, impeded in its passage in this vessel, must drive and buffet all the more into the next ones, until it has considerably dilated them to give itself room.

. . . . .

Compression of the aorta a little above the diaphragm causes an accumulation, in the upper organs only, of the blood due to the whole body and accurately apportioned to the vessels as a whole; it therefore brings ruin and calamity to the head and to the heart. If, on the other hand, the vena cava is tightly ligatured a little above the diaphragm—where it passes towards the heart in a trunk which is free and unconnected with any other organs—so that the passage of blood through it is instantly suppressed, the amount of harm this means for the animal can scarcely be told. For, though it reveals no feeling of pain or torment by struggling or howling as a result of the application of the ligature to the vein, it nevertheless soon begins to weaken, and to become exhausted to such a degree, that it can scarcely stand on its feet. . . .

III. We have next to explain how far the blood may be regarded as responsible, and by what defect in it the heart's movement is impaired.

It disturbs the heart's movement in three ways in particular:

1. By solidification and coagulation.
2. By being present in excess.
3. By being present in subnormal amount.

. . . . .

IV. Let it suffice to have shown hitherto how much the heart's movement is changed by the heart itself, or by its vessels, or by the blood. It remains for me lastly to explain how its movement is changed by variation in the inflow of spirits.

The orderly movement of the heart depends on the due inflow of spirits through the nerves, and so the movement of the heart will be very greatly changed by variation in their inflow.

1. The movement of the heart is accelerated in violent exercise in proportion as the blood is driven and poured into its ventricles in greater abundance as a result of the movement of the muscles. The heart must pass on the blood as fast as it receives it, and so it distributes it in larger amount to the brain as well as to the other organs. To discharge a mutual obligation, the spirits are likewise sent out in larger amount to hasten the movement of the heart. In fevers, also, the movement of the heart is remarkably accelerated, not because the blood boils out fiercely into the aorta, but because its heat and feeling of warmth is inimical to the ventricles of the heart, and, transmitted to the cerebellum, excites the spirits to quicken the heart's movement for its expulsion; partly, too, because some very fierce, uncurbed portions of the blood are deposited in the brain, and stir up the spirits dwelling there to a state of excitement: just as the movement of the heart is surprisingly increased through drinking good wine or any highly spirituous beverage, because the spirituous portions are distilled in large amount from such liquids into the brain, and excite the spirits dwelling in the brain to similar disorders.

2. The movement of the heart is diminished in large haemorrhages, fastings, long-continued illness or grief of any kind, prolonged lassitude, fainting disorders, and malign fevers: inasmuch as the blood, through deficiency in total amount, or through lack of fresh food, or through the ravages of long-continued fever, or its constitutional weakness, is so far degenerate and impoverished that its exhausted, effete, or aged mass is quite unequal to the distillation of spirits for the brain. . . .

3. It is perverted in emotional states, such as anger, joy, and sudden fright, when the spirits fly to the heart in excessive and unwonted amount or with a greater rush than usual, accelerate its movement very greatly, and excite and convulse it with bounding movements that are sometimes terrific. This condition writers have from time to time called by the diminutive term *palpitation,* not perhaps giving it adequate consideration; but actually the heart-muscle is subject

to the same ills as other muscles, just as it performs work identical with theirs. . . .

4. The spirits, then, in the brain and cerebellum sometimes overstimulate the heart-muscle, when they are driven to disordered activities. When, on the other hand, they are carried off and drawn away in another direction, this muscle is often contracted so tightly and firmly that it has no diastole for a long time. . . .

5. While the heart's movement ceases awhile when the spirits are drawn off elsewhere, it fails completely when their inflow is altogether cut off: as in Apoplexy.

· · · · · ·

2. While stagnation and clotting of the blood are induced by a small, weak movement of the heart, the mixture of the blood is best maintained, on the other hand, when the heart's movement is vigorous and strong. But, if the movement becomes violent, the blood-fluid is very greatly thinned as a result of the extreme shaking it receives, and hence sweating occurs on exercise, bathing, and dry or steam sweating-baths. If this excessive activity is occasioned for too long a time and to an undue extent, the blood is deprived of its means of transport through loss of serum, and is rendered unfit for circulation; and the heart itself becomes tired in its work through the loss of spirits. As a result fainting and syncope occur.

These are the symptoms and effects which redound most directly on the blood itself through alteration in this way or that of the heart's movement. There are, however, other things which affect equally the organs containing the blood.

1. When the movement of the heart is weak and intermittent, it predisposes to such head affections as vertigo, scotoma, blindness, and fainting. The reason for these symptoms lies in the fact that the animals spirits and life itself depend on a continuous supply of blood to the brain.

· · · · · ·

But for the careful estimation of the blood-flow and its remarkable rapidity it will be sufficient to quote one single experiment. I divided both cervical arteries in a fair-sized dog, and at the same time I compressed the trunk of the aorta below the heart with a finger, which I passed through an aperture made in the left side of the chest near the heart, so that no blood should pass down the aorta; finally, I took care to constrict the brachial arteries below the axillae. As a result practically all the blood (except that passing through the vertebrals) was expelled from the heart by way of the cervical arteries; and, strange to say, it all flowed out within three minutes; so that it cannot be denied that the whole mass of it had passed through the heart in that time. One may, indeed, see in cases of trauma, which involve section of any large artery, how brief a period suffices for people so mutilated to lose their life and practically all their blood. This blood, however, must all have first circulated through the ventricles of the heart.

. . . . .

It is certain, then, that the difference in colour, which is found between venous and arterial blood, is quite independent of the heating of the blood in the heart (even if some such heating must be conceded there); for, granted that heating does occur chiefly in the heart, then, as the function of both ventricles is the same, and they do not differ in any other respects than, as stated above, in the strength and thickness of their fibres, why should the colour not undergo a similar change in the right ventricle? But it is quite certain that blood withdrawn from the pulmonary artery is similar in all respects to venous blood, and is only reddish on the surface. Indeed, it will be shown by a very convincing experiment that this fresh red colour is not conferred on the blood by the left ventricle either. For, if the trachea is exposed in the neck and divided, a cork inserted, and the trachea ligatured tightly over it to prevent any ingress of air into the lungs, then the blood flowing from a simultaneous cut in the cervical artery (or, at least, such blood as comes out some time after the asphyxiation of the lung) will be seen to be as completely venous and dark in colour, as if it had flown from a wound in the jugular vein. I have tried this fairly often, and the same truth is more evident still from the fact that the blood within the left ventricle of the heart and the trunk of the aorta of an animal, which has been strangled or has died a natural death, and in which air is prevented from passing into the blood, is found to be entirely akin to venous blood.

Finally, to abolish any possible room for doubt, it occurred to me to make an experiment on a strangled dog, after sensation and life had completely deserted it, and to see if the still-fluid blood in the vena cava would all return equally bright in colour through the pulmonary vein, after being driven to the right ventricle and to the lungs. So I drove on the blood, and carried out a simultaneous insufflation of the perforated lungs. The result corresponded very well with my expectation, for the blood was discharged into the dish as bright-red in colour, as if it were being withdrawn from an artery in a living animal.

I have shown that the bright red colour of arterial blood is not acquired through any heating in the heart or anywhere else at any time. In like manner also the dark colour of venous blood is independent of any extinction of its heat within the veins. For, if this were so, why should the arterial blood not take on a like colour after it has left its vessels, since it has now beyond all doubt lost its heat?

This being so, we must next see to what the blood is indebted for this deep red coloration. This must be attributed entirely to the lungs, as I have found that the blood, which enters the lungs completely venous and dark in colour, returns from them quite arterial and bright. For, if the anterior part of the chest is cut away and the lungs are continuously insufflated by a pair of bellows inserted into the trachea, and they are also pricked with a needle in various places to allow free passage of air through them, then, on the pulmonary vein being cut near the left auricle, the blood will flow out into a suitably placed receptacle completely bright-red in colour. And, as long as the lungs are supplied with fresh air in this way, the blood will rush out scarlet, until the whole perfusate reaches several ounces, nay pounds, just as if it were being received from a cut artery. What I had written earlier about the blood withdrawn from the pulmonary vein being like venous blood was said as a result of experimental work, but at a time when I did not yet known from experiment that one could keep life in an animal by continuous insufflation of pricked lungs; so that all the air had been forced out of the lung before I was able to seize and to lance the pulmonary vein. I acknowledge my indebtedness to the very famous Master *Robert Hooke* for this experiment—by which the lungs are kept continuously dilated for a long time without meanwhile endangering the animal's life—and the opportunity thereby given me to perform this piece of work.

• • • • • •

Indeed, if the cake of blood is turned over after remaining stationary for a long while, its outer and uppermost layer takes on the red colour in a short space of time (provided the blood is still fresh). It is a matter of common knowledge that venous blood becomes completely red when received into a dish and shaken up for a long time to cause a thorough penetration of air into it. And let no one be surprised at a loss or admixture of air causing such marked colour-changes in the blood, since we see other fluids also acquiring various colorations, according as their pores take up or refract in greater or lesser amount the rays of light.

If you ask me for the paths in the lungs, through which the nitrous spirit of the air reaches the blood, and colours it more deeply, do you in turn show me the little pores by which that other nitrous spirit, which exists in snow, passes into the drinks of gourmets and cools their summer wines. For, if glass or metal connot prevent the passage of this spirit, how much more easily will it penetrate the looser vessels of the lungs? Finally, if we do not deny the outward passage of fumes and of serous fluid, why may we not concede an inward passage of this nitrous foodstuff into the blood through the same or similar little pores?

On this account it is extremely probable that the blood takes in air in its course through the lungs, and owes its bright colour entirely to the admixture of air. Moreover, after the air has in large measure left the blood again within the body and the parenchyma of the viscera, and has transpired through the pores of the body, it is equally consistent with reason that the venous blood, which has lost its air, should forthwith appear darker and blacker.

From this it is easy to imagine the great advantage accruing to the blood from the admixture of air, and the great importance attaching to the air taken in being always healthy and pure; one can see, too, how greatly in error are those, who altogether deny this intercourse of air and blood. Without such intercourse, any one would be able to live in as good health in the stench of a prison as among the most pleasant vegetation. Wherever, in a word, a fire can burn sufficiently well, there we can equally well breathe. . . . With regard to our next subject, *The Transfusion of blood from one animal to another,* I do not know if the hope of accomplishing this, or the thought of trying it, occurred to any one earlier than three years ago. For, even after it was openly suggested as likely to have great applications in medicine, most people, nevertheless, withheld their hands completely from the experiment, or moved them to it in vain, either through fear of the operative difficulty, or in discouragement at its strangeness. . . .

For many years at Oxford I saw others at work, and myself, for the sake of experiment, injected into the veins of living animals various opiate and emetic solutions, and many medicinal fluids of that sort. The technical procedure for this is now quite well known, and this is not the place to describe the individual results and outcomes of these experiments. But when, in addition, I likewise injected many nutrient solutions, and had seen the blood of different animals mix quite well and harmoniously with various injections of wine and beer, it soon occurred to me to try if the blood of different animals would not be much more suitable and would mix without danger or conflict. And, because in shed blood (no matter how well coagulation should be guarded against by repeated shaking) the natural blending and texture of the parts must of necessity change, I thought it much more convenient to transfer the unimpaired blood of an animal, which was still alive and breathing, into another. I thought this would be more easily effected, inasmuch as the movement of blood through its vessels is so rapid and swift, that I had observed almost the whole mass of blood flow out in a few second, where an outlet offered. Taking hope from this, I turned mind and hands to put the matter to a practical test.

And first I tried to transfer blood from the jugular vein of one animal to the jugular vein of a second by means of tubes between the two; but, seeing the blood clot at once in the tube and block its own passage on account of the slow movement of the venous blood, I soon began to try another way, and guided, as it were, by nature herself, I finally determined to transfer blood from an artery of one animal into a vein of a second; and by this new device to extend the circulation of the blood beyond the boundaries prescribed for it.

As everything answered expectation as I wished, I finally showed this new experiment at Oxford towards the end of February 1665, in an interesting demonstration and under the most happy circumstances. There were present the learned Doctor *John Wallis, Savilian* Professor of Mathematics, *Thomas Millington,* Doctor of Medicine, and other Doctors of the same University.

. . . . .

Transfusion was therefore first performed by me at the end of February 1665, the *Honourable Boyle's* letter was given to me on the 6th of the *following June,* and my reply was inserted next *December* in the *Philosophical Transactions,* which were then going to press. Denis, on the other hand, made no mention of transfusion until a whole year later, and, further, he himself admits (though he says he had thought of it ten years before) that he learned first from philosophical books the possibility of transfusion and the technique for its achievement. I therefore leave it to others to judge who should receive the credit for the discovery of this experiment. . . . I have no doubt that this discovery, whose soever it is, will be employed with great profit for the human race, if it is practised with due consideration and care.

For there is no reason to think that the blood of other animals mixes less well with human blood than with animal blood. This view is abundantly confirmed by recent experiments of French workers, and I also found it so not very long ago in the case of a certain *A.C.*, who was the subject of a harmless form of insanity. I superintended the introduction into his arm at various times of some ounces of sheep's blood at a meeting of the *Royal Society*, and that without any inconvenience to him. In order to make further experiments on him with some profit also to himself, I had decided to repeat the treatment several times in an effort to improve his mental condition; he, on the other hand, consulted his instinct rather than the interests of his health, and completely eluded our expectations.

Every one, however, is not equally qualified to receive the blood of others, and no treatment is so useful that its rash and unsuitable administration does not easily bring it into disrepute. I think, therefore, that it will be worth while for me to intimate briefly, in a few words only, the sort of cases and the condition of health most suitable for the employment of transfusion.

Patients, whose blood is definitely putrid and has been long corrupt, or is very deeply tainted by a poisonous ferment from without, those, too, whose viscera are polluted and spoilt, as sometimes happens in cases of scurvy, venereal disease, leprosy, poisoning, or long-continued illness, cannot hope for any benefit or help from transfusion.

The Modern Approach of Lower

Richard Lower (1632–91) studied medicine at Oxford and became one of the most famous medical practitioners in London and a Fellow of the newly founded Royal Society. He was in direct contact with John Mayow, Robert Hooke, and Robert Boyle and knew, of course, of their work on the lungs and respiration, changing air pressures and volumes by chemical or mechanical means. Since he was one of the first persons to perform transfusions and the first physician to use them on human patients, it is not surprising to learn of his conviction that "by exchanging the blood of old and young, sick and healthy, hot and cold, fierce and fearful, tame and wild animals," great transformations in the well-being and conduct of the recipients could be attained. But Lower's chief research was on the nature of the changes in the blood occurring in the complex networks of capillaries within the lungs. Hooke, too, had considered this subject and in his usual manner had conducted some quick and insightful preliminary experiments.

Although Lower accepted the prevailing theories of disease and prescribed treatments that seem odd or superstitious today, such as phlebotomy, regimen, and herbs, his book *On the Heart* is suffused with a thoroughly modern spirit, as the excerpt well illustrates. Since even before the time of Harvey, revolutionary ideas had been sporadically springing up in many sectors of biology without any immediate impact on the basic concepts of medicine. The studies of Lower and his successor, John Mayow, demonstrated a strong tendency actually to apply the new ideas to medicine and surgery. The results were brilliant and full of potential for further advance.

It is interesting to note how painstakingly the human mind had to struggle for even small bits of knowledge that to later generations appear both simple and obvious. Such questions as whether the heart's motions are caused by the "ebullition of the blood" within it or by the heat and whether the blood's heat is produced by the heart itself or by the lungs were major puzzles that required reasonable answers. In fact, so many new phenomena and tools had invaded the field normally covered by the established belief-web—the set of notions on air as an element and on the role of blood in the body—that its authority vanished, and clever pioneers could roam where they willed. The situation was no different from the one resulting in geographical explorations and discoveries, with which it coincided. Even under normal conditions, no conceptual scheme is completely free of gaps, weak links, contradictions, or plain exceptions to the rule. And the post-Harvey era in biology was exceptionally lively, challenging, conducive to inquiry, and rewarding to the curious. The wide range of the topics investigated testifies to the intellectual vitality of the period.

Lower's writings show his vision and skill and the scope of his mental probings, rapidly translated into practical tests. On the matter of nerve function, what he has to say is reasonable and valid. It is clear from the text that what we call the nerve impulse he designates as animal spirits, which, he states, may cease to "trickle down the nerves from the brain" if the blood supply to that vital organ is interrupted. The important point here is his belief that the nerves convey something to the organs to which they are joined. That his terminology is less explicit than ours in no way detracts from the brilliance of his deductions on the accelerated movement of the heart, the relation of the heartbeat to emotional states, and the causes of heart failure. Nor does his ignorance of oxygen and oxidation, or oxygenation, prevent him from pursuing his pathfinding studies on the different colors of the venous and arterial blood streams. In a few paragraphs he recounts how he established that the brightening of the color of arterial blood is independent of the state of being alive and is dependent wholly upon exposure to air in the lungs. Not satisfied, he carries out many other experiments to verify his finding and place it upon as sound a footing as possible. The idea of gaseous exchange emerges merely as a flash of thought. Yet this idea is destined to affect deeply future research.

Because of the blood's aura of mystery, or perhaps because of technical difficulties, the practice of transfusion was approached with hesitancy and caution. However, once Christopher Wren conceived of injecting fluid into the blood stream, Lower's injection of blood was inevitable, and so was the next step, transfusion from one live organism to another. Note that Lower's first patient was a mental case and that the job was done "in an effort to improve his mental condition." The inadequate pattern of beliefs upon which his motive for experimentation rested actually may have promoted progress, for if medicine had not assigned to blood direct power over sanity and insanity, it is very likely that Lower might not have performed the transfusion. Although the entire effort was soon abandoned, the memory of it remained, and so a return to it later on was greatly facilitated.

16. JOHN MAYOW

Medico-Physical Works

[TRACTATUS QUINQUE MEDICO-PHYSICI]

Every one knows that when we inspire, air rushes into the expanded chest and inflates the lungs. But authorities are not equally agreed as to the cause of the air rushing in with such vehemence. Some account for it by a vacuum and an attraction of I know not what imaginary sort.

Others again suppose that the air about the chest, pushed forward by its expansion, propels that which is next it, and this again the next; and that so the propulsion goes on, and thus at last the air near the mouth is driven into the lungs.

· · · · ·

With respect, then, to the entrance of the air into the lungs, I think it is to be maintained that it is caused in the following manner by the pressure of the atmosphere. For as the air, on account of the weight of the superincumbent atmosphere, not only rushes into all empty places, but also presses forcibly upon whatever is next it (as Boyle's experiments have put beyond doubt), it follows that the air, passed through the nostrils and the trachea, up to the bronchia or gates of the lungs, presses against the lungs from

From *Medico-Physical Works,* London, 1674, reprinted by University of Chicago Press, Chicago, 1908, pp. 183–210 (Second Treatise on Respiration).

within and seeks an entrance into them. Hence it is that when the inner sides of the thorax (which by compressing the lungs from without were resisting the pressure of this air) are drawn outwards by muscles whose function it is to dilate the chest, and the space in the thorax is enlarged, the air which is nearest the bronchial inlets, now that every obstacle is removed, rushes under the full pressure of the atmosphere into the cavities of the lungs, and by inflating them occupies and fills the space of the expanded chest.

The structure of the lungs is adapted for their inflation as thus described, for their substance is composed, as the eminent Dr. Malpighi has noted, of very fine membranes, which form an almost infinite number of spherical vesicles whose mutual connection is such that there is easy access from the trachea to those nearest to it, and from these again to others. Consequently when these vesicles are inflated by an inrush of air, the whole substance of the lungs must necessarily expand.

· · · · ·

And indeed the force with which air that has not yet expanded seeks to enlarge its volume, is exactly equal to the pressure of the atmosphere, inasmuch as it depends upon it, and increases or diminishes according as this pressure is greater or less. For the elastic force of the air seems to be due to this, that the air, especially that near the earth, is compressed and its volume diminished by the weight of the superincumbent air; hence it is that it always strives to expand, just as a fleece, when the force which compressed it is withdrawn, instantly unfolds and expands with a certain motion of restitution. And this can be confirmed by a well enough known experiment.

For if a bladder with most of the air pressed out of it, and tied by a tight ligature round the sphincter, be placed in a glass from which the air is afterwards exhausted, we shall at once see the bladder swell and become greatly distended, a rather pretty sight by the way. For although a very little air was contained in the bladder, yet when the external air (by the pressure of which it was reduced to small volume) is removed, it immediately expands and inflates the bladder, indeed sometimes violently bursts it. And, in fact, the inflation of the lungs is effected in a not very different way. For as soon as the sides of the thorax (which by compressing the lungs make them shrink) are drawn outwards, the air at the entrance to the lungs is immediately driven into them, whether by atmospheric pressure or in consequence of its own elastic force, and distends them.

* * * * *

And indeed although the lungs were provided with muscles, under their contractile action the lungs would not expand but rather contract, as happens to the bladder and stomach, and other organs of the kind. And further, when the thorax is pierced, the lungs immediately collapse at that place—a clear proof certainly that their movement is not spontaneous, but depends entirely on that of the chest. As for the nerves which are distributed in the trachea and bronchia, they do not serve for movement, but for sensation and the nutrition of these organs.

* * * * *

Here, by the way, surgeons should be warned not to close the wound if the chest has been perforated except when the thorax is contracted to the utmost; for, otherwise, if the opening made by the wound is closed when the chest is dilated (that is, when the air has filled the interior cavity of the thorax), it will be impossible for the chest to contract on account of the resistance of the air inside, or for the lungs to expand, except partially, and, in consequence, suffocation will necessarily follow.

Now that it has been shown that the entrance of air into the lungs depends upon the dilatation of the chest, it remains for investigation how the chest is expanded. And here, following not so much the authority of writers as the truth, I shall state briefly what the thing itself teaches.

The received opinion is that of the intercostal muscles, only the external serve to dilate the chest, while the internal, on the other hand, contract it. But it seems to me more reasonable to suppose that the chest is dilated simultaneously by both. And that this may be better understood I shall premise the following observations.

We may affirm that the raising of the ribs dilates the space within the chest and that their depression diminishes it. For we suppose here (what any one may see in a skeleton) that the ribs (especially the lower, which contribute most to the dilatation of the chest) are not articulated to the spine and sternum at right angles, but that the angles below the ribs are a little less than right angles; so that if a rib is raised, its articulations with the spine and sternum will approach to right angles. We assert further that the chest is dilated by the ribs when raised to right angles. . . . And thus it is clear that one half of the chest is expanded by the ribs being raised towards right angles, and it is evidently the same with the other side. As for the false ribs, although their extremities are connected not with the sternum but with the diaphragm, they have notwithstanding the same motion, and in like manner dilate the chest. But since the ribs when drawn upwards approach nearer to right angles with the spine, and the ribs when raised to right angles open up a space in the thorax, it follows that when the ribs are drawn upwards they dilate the chest, which is what we undertook to prove. Nay, any one can experience in himself that the ribs are drawn upwards in inspiration and the dilatation of the chest, but that they descend in expiration and the contraction of the chest.

This premised, if the ribs are raised by the intercostal muscles, even the internal ones (which has next to be proved), it follows necessarily that the chest is dilated by their contraction.

· · · · ·

It is probable then that, in expiration, the parts of the thorax return, by a movement of restitution, to their natural position without any aid from the muscles. For it is difficult and contrary to their natural position for the ribs to be drawn upwards, so that for this there is indispensable need of the twofold and united action of both sets of muscles, the internal and the external. But the ribs sink down again, without any work, as is clear in the case of a dead animal or a skeleton. Wherefore there is no reason for saying that Nature has provided as much muscular power for the latter action, which is clearly no action, as for the former, which is indeed a very difficult one.

. . . . .

Besides the aforesaid muscles, the diaphragm also contributes to the expansion of the chest, and indeed ordinary inspiration seems to be mainly caused by it. In expiration the diaphragm being in diastole, and released from constriction and in a flaccid condition, is pushed upwards into the region of the thorax by the stomach and the other viscera contained in the abdomen; whence it is that it compresses the lungs and diminishes the space in the chest. But in inspiration the diaphragm is in systole, and contracted, so that it no longer remains greatly curved but is carried downwards and outwards as it flattens. So that the viscera of the abdomen, which were previously contained in its concavity, are, now that it has contracted, forced both downwards and outwards, and the space in the thorax which was previously occupied by the diaphragm and the said viscera is now left free for the expansion of the lungs. And indeed any one can feel in himself that the ribs rise in inspiration, while the viscera of the abdomen move both downwards and outwards under the pressure of the diaphragm. But all this will be more evident from an autopsy, for if the chest of any animal is opened and the diaphragm pressed downwards by the hand while the ribs are pulled upwards (and this is not done without much exertion), you will see that the chest dilates and that its capacity is enlarged. But as soon as the supporting force is withdrawn, the chest will of itself contract anew. For the diaphragm, pushed by the viscera in the lower part of the belly, will soon rise into the cavity of the chest, and the ribs, by descending forcibly to their natural position, will still further diminish the cavity of the thorax.

Hence if the stomach be too full, or if the liver or the rest of the viscera are much enlarged, respiration cannot go on except with difficulty, inasmuch as the said viscera, from their mass, press so much on the diaphragm as to prevent it from descending and enlarging the cavity of the chest. Still if, owing to an urgent necessity for more vigorous breathing, the violent contraction of the diaphragm forces the abdominal viscera downwards, nothwithstanding their resistance, it not infrequently happens that its fibres contract too much in consequence of the violent strain, so that their tone is almost destroyed and respiration goes on afterwards with difficulty.

$$* \quad * \quad * \quad * \quad *$$

And quite similarly in the hysteric passion, when the organs in the lower part of the belly, convulsed and swollen, rise in a mass, and keep the diaphragm up, respiration must necessarily cease and suffocation follow, as it does.

$$* \quad * \quad * \quad * \quad *$$

It seems to be different in the case of that oppression at night, with difficult respiration, which is called nightmare; for this state seems to be produced not by a convulsion of the parts about the thorax but by an impediment to the proper influx of spirits. This oppression generally attacks those who are falling asleep. For when sleep begins, the spirits which are the instruments of voluntary functions, retire towards the cerebrum, or at least no longer flow copiously from it. Meanwhile the spirits which have for their office involuntary actions and natural movements issue in continual flow either from the cerebrum or from the cerebellum. If, however, in consequence of any confusion, or from morbid matter causing disordered movement of the spirits, those of the latter kind as well as the former, while sleep is coming on, return towards the brain and are detained there, not only voluntary, but also natural actions are necessarily interrupted by the flow of spirits being impeded. Hence the actions of the heart, the thorax, and indeed of the whole body cease, so that the patient is necessarily affected with the very greatest oppression, suffocation, and a kind of immobility.

$$* \quad * \quad * \quad * \quad *$$

From this we gather that laughter takes place without any action or contraction of the diaphragm. For in laughter the diaphragm is not, as some have supposed, drawn upwards when contrated by repeated irritations. For in systole and in its contraction, it is drawn downwards, as shown above, and so causes inspiration rather than that expiration which takes place in laughter. . . . For it has been shown that laughter does not proceed from the action or systole of the diaphragm, but, on the contrary, from its diastole.

We have spoken thus far of the manner in which respiration takes place, and it now remains for us to inquire into its use. This is indeed a most difficult affair, for there is not more accord as to its necessity than doubt as to its use.

For not only is air inspired useful for tasting and smelling, and expelled, for talking, shouting, coughing, sneezing, and spitting, and again, when retained, for the expulsion of urine and fæces, for parturition, and for moving on the chyle, the lymph, and the blood; the breath we inspire is destined for a still nobler use: from which arises such a necessity of drawing breath that we cannot indeed live a moment without it.

Some suppose that respiration chiefly serves for cooling the heart; but heating rather than such a cooling seems to suit the circulation and fermentation of the blood. . . .

But the prevalent opinion is that respiration is necessary to life in order that the blood may be able to pass through the lungs from the right ventricle of the heart into the left. For the fœtus in the uterus, whose blood does not pass through the lungs but through special ducts, does not need to breathe at all. And this they say is the reason why there is not the same necessity for breathing in the uterus as after birth.

But there is no reason why we should say that Nature has constructed the lungs with so much skill and labour only that the blood may pass through them after birth, since it might pass by a shorter and much less obstructed road through the same channels it follows in the unborn fœtus. Nay, it is the case that the blood can pass through the lungs apart from their motion. For if blood or any other liquid is injected by means of a syringe into the pulmonary artery of a dead animal it will pass readily enough into the left ventricle of the heart. And indeed any one can feel for himself that although respiration be temporarily suspended, yet the pulse of the arteries in the wrist is strong enough. . . .

Hence some think that respiration serves a further purpose, that of churning, forsooth, and dividing into the smallest particles the thicker venous blood. For otherwise (as they say) the blood would be separated into distinct parts, namely, serum and a purple sediment. But neither is this the chief use of respiration.

. . . . .

For if, by means of bellows attached to the trachea of an animal, a dog for example, the lungs are inflated, but in such a way that, through openings made here and there at their extremities, some of the air may pass out, the loss of which must be supplied by the bellows that the lungs may not collapse; in this case, I say, the animal will live. . . . But if, on the other hand, the mouth and nose be closed after breath is taken and drawn into the lungs, death will certainly follow, although the lungs remain inflated, because expiration is prevented. . . . But the reason that an animal lives in the one case and dies in the other is that in the former there is a continual access of fresh air, but none in the latter.

. . . . .

Let us now inquire what the aërial element is which is so necessary to life that we cannot live for even a moment without it. And indeed it is probable that certain particles of a nitro-saline nature, and these very subtle, agile, and in the highest degree fermentative, are separated from the air by the action of the lungs and conveyed into the mass of the blood. For this aërial salt is so necessary to every form of life that not even plants can grow in soil to which air has not access. But if such soil be exposed to the air and impregnated anew with this fertilising salt, it will again become suitable for the nourishment of plants. So that even plants themselves seem to have a kind of respiration and the necessity of absorbing air.

But it is not so easy to understand the function which this aërial salt exercises in animal life, yet it is probable that nitro-aërial spirit, mixed with the saline-sulphureous particles of the blood, excites in it the necessary fermentation. And yet it is not to be supposed that this effervescence of the blood takes place in the heart alone, but that it goes on first in the pulmonary vessels and afterwards in the arteries no less than in the heart. For I do not recognise that ferment, I know not what, in the left ventricle of the heart. For whence and by what vessels is there so great an influx of it as would suffice for heating so often every day the whole mass of the blood? In the fœtus the blood to a great extent passes directly from the right ventricle of the heart into the aorta, and yet this ought not to be done if so necessary a fermentation took place in the left ventricle. Much less probable is it that the beating of the heart is caused by the rarefaction of the blood in its ventricles as the famous Descartes supposed. For if the pulsation of the heart were caused by the fermentation of the blood in its cavities, then, when the heart beat, its ventricles would be greatly dilated by that blood, just as a bladder is blown into the form of greatest capacity. . . .

So that obviously the heart seems to be nothing but a muscle, differing but little in its action from other muscles, and we must believe its function to consist in contraction alone and the expulsion of the blood.

But although nitro-aërial particles excite fermentation in the mass of the blood, I do not know whether it is owing to the want of them that the blood, immediately upon respiration being checked, becomes so thick that it is quite incapable of motion, and stagnates in the left ventricle of the heart. . . .

Life, if I am not mistaken, consists in the distribution of the animal spirits, and their supply is most of all required for the beating of the heart and the flow of blood to the brain. And it appears that respiration chiefly conduces to the motion of the heart in the manner to be stated elsewhere. For it is probable that this aërial salt is altogether necessary for every movement of the muscles; so that without it there could be no pulsation of the heart.

For if it be allowed that the sudden contraction of the muscles results from the intermixture of particles of different kinds, mutually moving each other, then it is scarcely to be supposed that the particles of both kinds, by the effervescence of which the contraction of the muscles is caused, proceed from the mass of the blood; for liquids derived from the same source reunite without any effervescence, so that it appears that something extraneous is required for the production of the motive fermentation.

We may then suppose that nitro-saline particles derived from the inspired air constitute the one kind of motive particles, and that these, when they meet the others, the saline-sulphureous particles supplied by the mass of the blood and residing in the motor parts, produce the effervescence from which muscular contraction results, as will be shown more fully in another place.

. . . . . .

Wherefore on the suppression of respiration, as that aërial salt required for any motion fails, the beating of the heart and, consequently, the flow of blood to the brain will necessarily be interrupted and death will ensue. But one may live for a certain time without breathing, because the blood contained in the pulmonary vessels and sufficiently impregnated with air is capable of moving the heart at least for a moment.

. . . . . .

Furthermore, if after the motion of the heart has ceased from the stopping of respiration, air is blown in through a tube fitted to the *vena cava*, we shall see the heart's motion re-established. So that it appears that air is that without which the movements of the heart cannot go on at all. Nor does it matter much how the air is transmitted to the mass of the blood, whether by the lungs or by any other way.

Mayow Explores the Mechanism of Respiration

John Mayow (1643-79) and Richard Lower had much in common. Both were products of the same highly active period in English science; both were members of the Royal Society; both achieved fame as medical practitioners; and both included in their circles of friends such men as Christopher Wren, Robert Boyle, Isaac Newton, and Robert Hooke. All the treatises that Mayow ever wrote, five in number, are contained in the volume from which the excerpt given here is taken. They are uniformly of the highest quality.

Mayow had clear insight into almost every problem he considered. He is aware of the true meaning of atmospheric pressure and applies it to the phenomenon of breathing, making use of the latest findings of Boyle and Malpighi. His model of an air-filled, closed bladder within a container that is first emptied of air and then refilled with air, so that the bladder expands and shrinks, is still employed as the best demonstration of the mechanism of breathing. His elaboration of the workings of the ribs, the two sets of intercostal muscles, and the diaphragm in inspiration and expiration constituted a masterly feat.

Wherever possible Mayow points to lessons for medicine and surgery. He presents a plethora of examples dealing with medical cases entailing one aspect or another of his animal experiments. However, like Dr. Lower, he also includes solid segments of a now-abandoned belief-pattern, as when he attributes nightmares to "an impediment to the proper influx of spirits" or describes the nature of sleep. In reality the outmoded explanation is of little consequence, for Mayow is a keen observer and a visionary interpreter, regardless of the particular set of rules under which he functions.

Although he studies the actual process of respiration directly by skillfully noting the movement of the ribs, the muscles, and the diaphragm, in his discussion of the purpose or use of respiration his approach has to be more speculative. Here he displays his genius at discerning situations by reason and intuition, in this instance exactly a century before the first evidence was forthcoming. He suggests that the element oxygen of the air interacts with some chemical constituent of the blood. The contact of air and blood occurs in the lungs. Thus he concludes that the lungs are necessary for the aeration of the blood or, as he puts it, to permit the nitro-aerial particles of the air to interact with the saline-sulphureous particles of the blood. He reports elsewhere that the nitro-aerial particles are apparently needed for both the burning of a candle and animal respiration, a possibility proposed as well by Boyle and others. Place both a candle and an animal in a closed chamber containing air; the candle will soon be extinguished, and shortly thereafter the animal will die. Place an animal alone in the same closed chamber, without a candle, and the animal will live twice as long before expiring as the animal with a candle. Obviously both candle and animal require the same air constituent. Equally perceptive are Mayow's remarks concerning the dependence of all muscles upon the availability of these vital nitro-aerial particles.

The postulation of an invisible component of the air turned out to be correct. Yet it was reasoned into existence in the same manner as Galen's septal pores. When a claim is verified by subsequent investigations, its author is lauded and applauded. When it proves deceptive, he is regarded as unsound and unscientific, even though his hypothesis seemed most reasonable at the time and might actually have stimulated much valuable experimentation.

17. ROBERT BOYLE

Suspicions About Some Hidden Qualities in the Air

Besides the four first qualities of the air, (heat, cold, dryness and moisture) that are known even to the vulgar; and those more unobvious, that philosophers and chemists have discovered, such as gravity, springiness, the power of refracting the beams of light, &c. I have often suspected, that there may be in the air some yet more latent qualities or powers differing enough from all these, and principally due to the substantial parts or ingredients, whereof it consists. And to this conjecture I have been led, partly (though not only, or perhaps chiefly) by considering the constitution of that air we live and breathe in, which, to avoid ambiguities, I elsewhere call atmospherical air. For this is not, as many imagine, a simple and elementary body, but a confused aggregate of effluviums from such differing bodies, that, though they all agree in constituting, by their minuteness and various motions, one great mass of fluid matter, yet perhaps there is scarce a more heterogeneous body in the world.

. . . . .

Now, among this multitude and variety

From *Tracts,* printed by W. G. and are to be sold by M. Pitt, London, 1674, pp. 1–71 (First Treatise).

of bodies, that lie buried out of our sight, who can tell, but that there may be some, if not many, of a nature very differing from those we are hitherto familiarly acquainted with; and that, as divers wonderful and peculiar operations of the loadstone, (though a mineral many ages ago famous among philosophers and physicians) were not discovered till of later ages, wherein its nobler virtues have been disclosed; so there may be other subterraneous bodies, that are endowed with considerable powers, which, if they were known, be found very differing from those of the fossils we are wont to deal with?

I also further consider, that (as I have elsewhere endeavoured to make it probable) the sun and planets (to say nothing of the fixed stars) may have influences here below distinct from their heat and light. On which supposition it seems not absurd to me to suspect, that the subtil, but corporeal, emanations even of these bodies may (sometimes at least) reach to our air, and mingle with those of our globe in that great receptacle or rendesvous of celestial and terrestrial effluviums, the atmosphere. . . .

And though the chief of the heteroclite effluviums, that endow the air with hidden qualities, may probably proceed from beneath the surface of the earth, and from the celestial bodies; yet I would not deny, but that, especially at some times, and in some places, the air may derive multitudes of efficacious particles from its own operations, acting as a fluid substance upon that vast number and variety of bodies, that are immediately exposed to it.

. . . . .

Besides the saline and sulphureous particles, that, at least in some places, may (as I have elsewhere shewn) impregnate the air, and give it a greater affinity to chemical menstruums more strictly so called; I am not averse from thinking, that the air, merely as a fluid body, that consists of corpuscles of differing sizes and solidities restlesly and very variously moved, may upon the account of these corpuscles be still resolving, or preying upon the particles of the bodies, that are exposed to their action. For many of those aerial corpuscles, some hitting and some rubbing themselves every minute against those particles of exposed bodies, that chance to lie in their way, may well, by those numerous occursions and affrictions, strike off and carry along with them now some, and then others of those particles; as you see it happens in water, which, as soft and fluid as it is, wears out such hard and solid bodies as stones themselves. . . .

Some things, that have occurred me, to have made me suspect, that it is not impossible, but that some bodies may receive a disposition to volatility, and consequently to pass into the air by the action of the sun-beams, in the form of sun-beams, or of some substance, that once issued out of the sun, and reached unto the air.

. . . . .

Having premised thus much to keep you from looking for stronger proofs than I think my task obliges me to give; the first phaenomenon, I shall propose, shall be the appearing or growth of some salts in certain bodies, which we observed to afford them either not at all, or at least nothing near in such plenty, or so soon, unless they be exposed to the air.

. . . . .

It may also be suspected, that the formerly mentioned salts found in marchasites, in nitrous and aluminous earths, &c. are made by the saline particles of the like nature, that among multitudes of other kinds swim in the air, and are attracted by the congenerous particles, that yet remain in the terrestrial bodies, that are, as it were, the wombs of such minerals, (as I have elsewhere shewn, that the spirit of nitre will, with fixed nitre and some other alkalies, compose salt-petre;) or else, that these aerial salts, if I may so call them, assisted by the moisture of the air, do soften and open, and almost corrode or dissolve the more terrestrial substance of these wombs, and thereby sollicit out and somewhat extricate the latent saline particles, and, by their union with them, compose those emerging bodies, that resemble vitriol, allum, &c.

. . . . .

The difficulty we find of keeping flame and fire alive,

though but for a little time, without air, makes me sometimes prone to suspect, that there may be dispersed through the rest of the atmosphere some odd substance, either of a solar, or astral, or some other exotic nature, on whose account the air is so necessary to the subsistence of flame; which necessity I have found to be greater, and less dependent upon the manifest attributes of the air, than naturalists seem to have observed. For I have found by trials purposely made, that a small flame of a lamp, though fed perhaps with a subtil thin oyl, would in a large capacious glass-receiver expire, for want of air, in a far less time than one would believe. . . . For after the extinction of the flame, the air in the receiver was not visibly altered, and, for aught I could perceive by the ways of judging I had then at hand, the air retained either all, or at least far the greatest part of its elasticity, which I take to be its most genuine and distinguishing property.

And this undestroyed springiness of the air seems to make the necessity of fresh air to the life of hot animals, (few of which, as far as I can guess after many trials, would be able to live two minutes of an hour, if they were totally and all at once deprived of air,) suggest a great suspicion of some vital substance, if I may so call it, diffused through the air, whether it be a volatile nitre, or (rather) some yet anonimous substance, sydereal or subterraneal, but not improbable of kin to that, which I lately noted to be so necessary to the maintenance of other flames.

· · · · ·

The ingenious Monsieur de Rocheford, in the handsome account he gives of the apple, or fruit of the tree junipa, whose juice is employed by the Indians to black their skins, that they may look the more terrible to their enemies, observes, that, though the stain, or, as he speaks, the tincture of this fruit cannot be washed out with soap, yet, within nine or ten days, it will vanish of itself; which would make one suspect, that there may be in the air some secret powerful substance, that makes it a menstruum of more efficacy than soap itself to obliterate stains. . . .

. . . I have several times made a substance, that consists chiefly of a metalline body, and is of a texture close enough to lie for many hours undissolved in a corrosive menstruum; and yet this substance, that was fixed enough to endure the being melted by the fire without losing its colour, would, when I had purposely exposed it to the air, be discoloured in a very short time, and have its superficial parts turned almost black.

. . . . .

On the other side I have often prepared a substance, whose effect appears quite contrary to this. For, though this factitious concrete, whilst kept to the fire, or very carefully preserved from the air, be of a red colour, almost like the common opacous bloodstone of the shops; yet, if I broke it, and left the lumps, or fragments of it, a little while in the air, it would in a short time (sometimes perhaps, not amounting to a quarter of an hour) it would, I say, have its superficial part turned of a dark colour, very little, and sometimes scarce at all, short of blackness.

A very inquisitive person of my acquaintance, having occasion to make, by distillation, a medicine of his own devising, chanced to observe this odd property in it, that, at that time of the year, if it were kept stopped, it would be coagulated almost like oil of anniseeds in cold weather: yet, if the stopple were taken out, and so access were for a while given to the air, it would turn to a liquor, and the vessel being again stopped, it would, though more slowly, recoagulate.

. . . . .

The other of the two phaenomena, I lately promised to mention, is afforded me by those various and odd diseases, that at some times, and in some places, happen to invade, and destroy numbers of beasts, sometimes of one particular kind, and sometimes of another. . . . And you will easily perceive, that some of these examples probably argue, that the subterraneal parts do sometimes (especially after earthquakes, or unusual cleavings of the ground) send up into the air peculiar kinds of venomous exhalations, that produce new and mortal diseases in animals of such a species, and not in those of another, and in this or that particular place, and not elsewhere.

. . . . .

And I remember, I desired some virtuosi of my acquaintance to assist me in the enquiry, whether any of the spots, that appear about the sun, may not, upon their sudden dissolution, have some of their discussed and dispersed matter thrown off, as far as to our atmosphere, and that copiously enough to produce some sensible alterations in it, at least as to gravity.

II. Another thing, that our two fore-mentioned suspicions, if allowed of, will suggest, is, that it may not seem altogether improbable, that some bodies, we are conversant with, may have a peculiar disposition and fitness to be wrought on by, or to be associated with, some of those exotic effluvia, that are emitted by unknown bodies lodged under ground, or that proceed from this or that planet. For what we call sympathies and antipathies depending indeed on the peculiar textures and other modifications of the bodies, between whom these friendships and hostilities are said to be exercised, I see not, why it should be impossible, that there be a cognation betwixt a body of a congruous or convenient texture, (especially as to the shape and size of its pores,) and the effluviums of any other body, whether subterraneal or sidereal. . . .

III. I now pass on to the other thing, that the two formerly mentioned suspicions may suggest, which is, that if they be granted to be well founded, we may be allowed to consider, whether among the bodies we are acquainted with here below, there may not be found some, that may be receptacles, if not also attractives, of the sidereal, and the other exotic effluviums, that rove up and down in our air.

. . . . .

And, without receding from the Corpuscularian principles, we may allow some of the bodies, we speak of, a greater resemblance to magnets, that what I have been mentioning. For not only such a magnet may upon the bare account of adhesion by juxta-position, or contact, detain the effluviums, that would glide along it, but these may be the more firmly arrested by a kind of precipitating faculty, that the magnet may have in reference to such effluviums; . . . .

Some Additional Experiments Relating to the Suspicions About the Hidden Qualities of the Air

EXPERIMENT IV

Because in most of the experiments of substances exposed to be impregnated by the air, or detain its saline or other exotic particles, we employed bodies prepared and much altered by the previous operation of the fire; we thought fit to make some trials with bodies unchanged by the fire; and to this purpose we took a marchasite, which was partly of a shining and partly of a darkish colour, and which seemed well-disposed to afford vitriol: of this we took several smaller lumps, that amounted to two ounces; these were kept in a room, where they were freely accessible to the air, which, by reason that the house, that was seated in the country, stood high, was esteemed to be very pure. After the marchasites had been kept in this room somewhat less than seven weeks, we weighed them again in the same balance, and found the two ounces to have gained above twelve grains in weight.

From *The Works of the Honourable Robert Boyle*, edited by T. Birch and printed for A. Millar, London, 1744, Volume III, pp. 474–5.

EXPERIMENT VII

We took, about the bigness of a nutmeg, of a certain soft but consistent body, that we had caused to be chemically prepared, and which, in the free air, would continually emit a thick smoke: this being put into a vial, and placed in a middle-sized receiver in our engine, continued for some time to afford manifest fumes, whilst the exhaustion was making; till at length, the air having been more and more pumped out, the visible ascention of fumes out of the vial quite ceased; and the matter having remained some time in this state, the smoking substance was so altered, that it would not emit fumes, not only when the air was let into the receiver, but not in a pretty while after the vial was taken out of it, till it had been removed to the window, where the wind blowing in fresh and fresh air, it began to smoke as formerly.

Physico-mechanical Experiments

41. To satisfy ourselves, in some measure, why respiration is so necessary to the animals, that nature hath furnish'd with lungs, we took a lark, one of whose wings had been broken by a shot; but, notwithstanding this hurt, the bird was very lively; and put her into the receiver, wherein she, several times, sprung up to a considerable height. The vessel being carefully closed, the pump was diligently ply'd, and the bird, for a while, appear'd lively enough; but, upon a greater exsuction of the air, she began manifestly to droop, and appear sick; and, very soon after, was taken with as violent, and irregular convulsions, as are observ'd in poultry, when their heads are wrung off, and died; (tho' when these convulsions appear'd, we let in the air,) with her breast upward, her head downward, and her neck awry; and this within ten minutes, part of which time had been employ'd in cementing the cover to the receiver. . . .

Then we put in a mouse, newly caught, and, whilst he was leaping up very high in the receiver, we fasten'd the cover to it;

From *The Philosophical Works of the Honourable Robert Boyle, Esq.*, edited by P. Shaw and printed for W. and J. Innys and J. Osborn and T. Longman, London, 1725, Volume II, pp. 407–651.

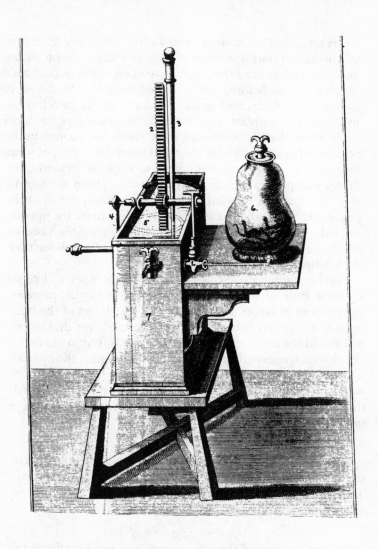

Robert Boyle's hand-operated vacuum pump. A cylinder (5) containing a piston is in the water tank (7). The piston is attached to the rack (2). STEP ONE: *Close the hole in the piston with the stopper* (3), *open the stopcock* (1), *and raise the piston with the crank* (4). *Air from the chamber* (6) *expands into the new space in the cylinder.* STEP TWO: *Close the stopcock* (1), *open the hole by removing the stopper* (3), *and lower the piston. Air trapped in the cylinder is forced out. Repeat.*

expecting, that an animal, used to live with very little fresh air, would endure the want of it better than the birds; but tho', for a while after the pump was set on work, he continu'd leaping up, as before; yet 'twas not long e'er he began to appear sick, giddy, and to stagger; after which, he fell down as dead, but without such violent convulsions as the birds had: when, hastily letting in some fresh air upon him, he recover'd his senses, and his feet, but seem'd to continue weak and sick; at length, growing able to skip, as formerly, the pump was ply'd again, for eight minutes; about the middle of which space, a very little air, by mischance, got in at the stop-cock; and, about two minutes after that, the mouse, several times, leap'd up lively; tho', in two minutes more, he fell down quite dead; yet with convulsions far milder than those wherewith the birds expired. . . .

Having caused these three creatures to be open'd, I could discover little of what we sought for, and might, possibly, have found in larger animals: for tho' the lungs of the birds appear'd very red, and, as it were, inflamed; yet that colour is usual in the lungs of such winged animals: but in almost all the destructive experiments, made in our engine, the animals appear'd to die with violent convulsive motions. From whence, whether physicians can deduce any thing towards the discovery of the nature of convulsive distempers, I leave to them to consider.

. . . . .

But, as to the reason why the inspiration, and expiration of air, are so very necessary to life, both naturalists, and physicians, differ so widely, that it will be very difficult, either to reconcile their opinions, or determine their controversies.

. . . . .

Now, to the first of these two ways, our engine affords us this objection; that upon the exsuction of the air, the animals die a great deal sooner, than if it were left in the vessel; tho', by that exsuction, the ambient space is left much more free to receive the steams, that are either breathed out of the lungs of the animal, or discharg'd by insensible transpiration.

But, if the hypothesis be taken in the other sense, it seems agreeable to that grand observation, which the phenomena of our engine, and the relations of travellers suggest, that there is a certain consistence of air, requisite to respiration; so that, if it be too thick, and already over-charg'd with vapours, it will be unfit to unite with, and carry off those of the blood; . . .

Now, that air too much thicken'd with steams, is unfit for respiration, appears by what happens in the lead-mines of Devonshire, and, perhaps, of some other countries; for, I am credibly inform'd that damps often rise here, which so thicken the air, as suddenly to stifle the workmen. And, that this proceeds, not from any arsenical, or poisonous exhalation contain'd in the damp; but, from too great a condensation of the air; seems probable, because it often leisurely extinguishes the flames of their candles, or lamps; and also, because in those cellars, where large quantities of new wine are set to work, men have been suffocated by the steams exhaling from the must, and too much thickening the air.

• • • • •

That air too much dilated, is unfit for respiration, the sudden death of animals kill'd in our exhausted receiver, sufficiently manifests. And, it may well be doubted, whether if a man were rais'd to the very top of the atmosphere, he would be able to live there many minutes. Josephus Acosta tells us, that when he himself pass'd the high mountains of Peru, to which, he says, the Alps seem'd but as ordinary houses, compared with high towers; he, and his companions were surpriz'd with extreme pangs of straining, and vomiting blood, and with so violent a distemper, that he concludes, he should undoubtedly have died, but, that this lasted not above three, or four hours, before they came into a more natural temperature of air. Our author adds, that he is, therefore, persuaded, "the element of the air is there so subtile, and delicate, as to be inconsistent with the respiration of man, which requires a more gross, and temperate air."

But, perhaps, the air doth something more, than barely help to carry off what is thrown out of the blood, in its passage thro' the lungs, from the right ventricle of the heart to the left.... Upon the whole, there appears reason to suspect, that there is some use of the air, which we do not yet thoroughly understand, that makes it so necessary to the life of animals.

Paracelsus, indeed, tells us, that "as the stomach concocts the aliment, and makes part of it useful to the body, rejecting the other; so the lungs consume part of the air, and reject the rest." Whence, according to him, we may suppose a little vital quintessence in the air, which serves to refresh and restore our vital spirits; for which purpose, the grosser, and far greater part of the air, being unserviceable, it is not strange that an animal should incessantly require fresh air. ... And, upon this supposition, Cornelius Drebell, is affirm'd, by many credible persons, to have contrived a vessel to be row'd under water; for Drebell conceiv'd, that, it is not the whole body of the air, but a certain spirituous part of it, that fits it for respiration; which being spent, the remaining grosser body of the air, is unable to cherish the vital flame residing in the heart. So that, besides the mechanical contrivance of his boat, he had a chymical liquor, which, by unstopping the vessel wherein it was contain'd the fumes of it would speedily restore to the air, foul'd by respiration, such a proportion of vital parts, as would make it again fit for that office; and having made it my business to learn this strange liquor, his relations constantly affirm'd, that Drebell would never disclose it, but to one person, who himself told me what it was.... We have made a hard body, in the form of a clove, but twice as long, and proportionably thick, of such a composition, that if it be kindled at the upper end, it will most certainly burn away to the bottom, much better than a match: this we often convey'd, kindled at the upper end, into a small receiver; but still found, that tho' presently, upon the exsuction of the air, it would leave smoking, and seem quite gone out; and again begin to smoke, as soon as the air was let in upon it; yet, if the air were kept out but four or five minutes, the fire would be totally, and irrecoverably extinguish'd.

. . . . .

It is much doubted, whether fish breathe under water.

That such as are not of the whale kind, have no respiration, as 'tis exercised by beasts, and birds, may be argued from their having no cavity in their hearts, and from their want of lungs, whence they are observ'd to be mute; unless we say, that their gills answer to lungs. But that air is necessary even to the lives of fish; and that therefore, 'tis probable, they have some obscure kind of respiration, seems manifest from observations, and experiments. Several authors tell us, that fish soon die in ponds, and glasses quite fill'd with water, if the one be so frozen over, and the other so closely stop'd, that they cannot enjoy the benefit of the air. And our engine hath taught us, that many little parcels of interspersed air, lurk in water; and this, perhaps, fish may make some use of.

Removing a large eel, out of a vessel of water, into our great receiver, we caused the air to be evacuated, and observ'd, that after some motion in the glass, she seem'd somewhat discomposed, and, at length, turn'd up her belly, and afterwards lay altogether moveless, as if quite dead; but upon taking her out of the receiver, she shew'd herself as much alive as before.

· · · · ·

Hippocrates, and some learned physicians of late, suppose, that a foetus respires in the womb; but it seems very difficult to conceive how air should traverse the body of the mother, and the teguments of the child: and since nature hath, in new-born infants, contrived peculiar temporary vessels, that the blood may circulate thro' other passages, than it does in the same individuals, when they come to have the free use of their lungs, 'tis improbable that the foetus in the womb should properly respire: but, then, since our experiments have manifested, that almost all kinds of liquors, as well as water, abound with interspersed corpuscles of air, it seems not altogther absurd, that when the foetus is grown big, it may exercise some obscure respiration; especially since children have been heard to cry in the mother's womb. . . . I have, also, had thoughts of trying to make a large receiver, with little glass windows, capable of holding a man, who may observe several things as to respiration, &c. and, in case of fainting, may, by giving a sign, be immediately relieved with fresh air. And it seems not impossible, that some men, by use, may bring themselves to support the want of air a pretty while; since we see that several will live much longer than others under water. Those who dive for pearls in the *West-Indies,* are reported to be able to stay a whole hour under water: and Cardan tells us of one Colanus, a diver in Sicily, who was able to continue there three or four times as long. . . .

However, there are but few men, who, even by use, can support for many minutes, the want of air: a famous diver, of my acquaintance, tells me, that at the depth of 50 or 60 feet under water, he cannot continue above two minutes, without resorting to the air which he carries down with him in an engine.

New Vistas Are Opened by Boyle

Men have always known that air was essential to life. It was, in fact, this common observation that was the basis of all postulations of antiquity concerning vital spirits, which the lungs presumably elaborated in the blood and sent to the heart via the pulmonary vein. Whether the elaboration was called vital spirits, pneuma, vitalized blood, or some other name, it was the same substance, resulting from what the lungs did to the blood before sending it to the left ventricle. The true nature of this action remained a mystery until the discovery of oxygen by Priestly and Lavoisier around 1775. It was the work of Robert Boyle, more than a century earlier, that successfully pointed the way for this momentous scientific event.

The heritage of Greek science regarded air as an element, along with earth, fire, and water. These substances were considered the basic constituents of matter, hence simple, homogeneous, and abundant. In actuality, air referred to gases, earth to solids, water to liquids, and fire to heat. Robert Boyle (1627–91) was one of the earliest men of science to challenge this basic faith in the four elements. He did it successfully, if wordily, in The Sceptical Chymist, first issued in 1661, and he continued his criticism in most of his later writings. Curiously enough, the excerpt presented here starts out with his apparent acceptance of the four qualities, another heritage of Greek science. Boyle was particularly qualified to tackle the problems of respiration because he had invented a vacuum machine, which, although very primitive, in that each stroke required manual adjustment, was still adequate to reveal significant new relationships.

In The Sceptical Chymist Boyle demonstrated the existence of compounds and elements, which rendered wholly unfeasible the concept of the four elements. He had encountered much and varied evidence that led him to regard air as a mixture rather than a simple element. On specious grounds, he had also come to view water as a mixture. Combining his opinions on air as a mixture with his experiments on vacua, he was indeed in a most favorable position to reach the conclusions here put forth.

The original papers from which the excerpt comes are quite long. Even with due allowances for Boyle's tendency to verbosity, they indicate that their author felt obliged to belabor his point because he knew that it would not be lightly received. Apparently ideas opposed to his own were firmly rooted in the dominant belief-web; obviously as long as air was thought of as an element, the notion of a distinct gaseous component possessing unique properties could not be accepted. Boyle engaged in a somewhat similar struggle when he sought to undermine the conception of fire as another of the four elements.

The fact is, however, that in Boyle's day the old pattern of beliefs had already been seriously damaged by attacks from other quarters. Paracelsus had freely hammered away at it, for good or for evil, and his total effect was highly stimulating. The iatrochemists carried on his battle, which often brought more chaos than clarity. Like rebellions and revolutions, these intellectual uprisings were better at demolishing than at mending or building. An established belief-web at the height of its power tends to be tyrannical and will often not even permit the emergence of a doubt or a divergent fact. Should a new datum or idea gain entry, it may be brushed aside with a slick rationalization. Only when a belief-web begins to show signs of senility does it become somewhat tolerant, relaxing its authority and allowing new information to penetrate its territory, to remain alive in it, and ultimately to assume control. The eradication and replacement of an old belief-pattern is a constructive process, like the removal of worn-out organic structures and compounds by bacteria and enzymes, which restore the constituent atoms to a state of freedom so that they can be employed again in novel combinations in unending cycles of growth and activity. Invariably the new ideas are richer and more complex than the old ones, and growth proceeds at a faster rate after demolition has begun than before. Thus Boyle acquits himself nobly of his thesis.

18. GIOVANNI ALFONSO BORELLI

On the Movements of Animals

[DE MOTU ANIMALIUM]

It is claimed by the ancients that the substance, structure, and action of the heart are different from those of other muscles. Other muscles are made to move by feeling and command, but the heart moves by an innate power. We believe the following to be demonstrated by recent investigations.

Proposition 77. *The immediate cause of the heart's movement is the same as that which moves limb muscles.*

Heart muscle is the same as other muscles, composed of muscle fascicles like them, disposed like them, and supplied with arteries and nerves in like manner. If one believes the heart to be moved by "spirits or vital power," the limb muscles must be likewise so moved. Thus, since all muscles contract by a violent agitation within their pores, the immediate cause of cardiac tension is the same—the ebullition and fermentation of blood from the affected regions by the agency of spiritual juices, pressing through the openings of the nerves. . . .

From *De Motu Animalium,* Lyons, 1685, Chapter VI, pp. 109–17, translated by M. Graubard.

Proposition 78. *The prime cause of heart motion is different from that which moves limb muscles.*

It is evident that the limb muscles of all animals are free to be moved whenever they wish to move them, to be kept in action for as long as desired, and to be halted when the action threatens to become a menace. But the heart muscle is not of this type; it does not obey the will, but continues to move whether we wish it or not, even in sleep. . . . Thus limb motion is termed voluntary, heart motion involuntary. . . .

Proposition 79. *The movement of the heart [seemingly] takes place because of organic necessity and automatically.*

It is stated that the cause of cardiac motion is the ebullition and fermentation of the blood, excited by action of the spiritual juice from the nerves. However, it is shown that pulsation persists even when the nerves from the brain are severed, so that the free will is destroyed and the nerve juices are interrupted. The prime cause is thus unknown and not perceivable but by analogy; we may say that it resembles force, the action of fire, the falling of a weight, the motion of water, and the like. We see the force of the wind moving clouds and causing vibrations on the surface of the water, not with a constant force but by vibration and wavelike oscillation. . . . The heart, similarly, moves not with fixed force but with the oscillation of the pendulum or of waves. . . .

It is learned from these findings and confirmed by experiment that in the brain the flow of spirits, always in fluid form, contacts and moistens the openings of nerves. Reaching out to the warm cavities in the spongy substance of the heart, this fluid moistens them with the spiritual juice, which flows with difficulty through the warm channels unless driven by energy or force, or by piercing the fibers themselves; but the juice itself is expressed drop by drop from the mass of the heart by peristaltic contractions, resulting from ebullition and violent movement on fusion of the juice with the crude humor of the blood.

Nor does the stimulation [by the juice] cease when the nerves are severed and the heart is cut out. Its pulsation continues for some time, since the lumens of the nerves joined to it remain filled with spiritual juice. . . .

It may indeed seem remarkable to some that a steady pulsation fails to occur in all muscles of the body, as it does in the heart, if the orifices of the nerves reaching the muscles of the body are always affected and moistened by the spiritual juice, as happens with the nerves of the heart.

This difficulty may be resolved if it is remembered that although orifices and canals are present in the nerves of the brain going to the muscles of the body, spiritual juice cannot be expressed from them into the muscles except following a convulsive movement of the spirit, which act is performed at the command of the will.

On the other hand, the orifices of the nerves in the heart remain open, just as in the ducts of a sponge, and produce a regular flow of drops by their fullness, which causes a steady twitching or convulsive movement. . . .

Proposition 80. *It is possible that the heart moves by virtue of the same animal faculty of perception but without conscious attention because of acquired habit.*

The pulsation of the heart may be caused by those animal powers that elicit the sensations of grief and joy, which spirits are transmitted to parts of the brain where the terminations of the nerves are agitated, those nerves chiefly gathering there which go out to the other muscles.

Since the sensitive power of the mind sends out spirits for the sensing of good and, if you will, evil, and if the organs of movement are then indeed those muscles that anticipate the greatest good or threaten with the worst evil, these should be excited most strongly while the heart is still beating gently; however, an increased pulsation is caused by the senses of understanding and feeling, which are the powers of apprehension of the mind. Thus the motion of the heart is controlled by the powers of understanding and feeling, not by an unknown instrument of fate. Yet, it seems unbelievable, that if the heart is moved only by one cause, it could be moved by others, and it will be agreed that the customary movements of the heart are made not by mechanical instruments, or automatically, but by the living powers of sense and desire, which bring about strong pulsations in joy and curtail pulsations in fear. . . .

The true reason why, in muscles in which motion is under the dictate of the will, movement persists for a long time after their separation from the animal is that powers and means are lodged in them—namely, the fibres, nerves, and the juices that they had received from the will of the animal, which, by their presence and stimulating effects cause movement, just as the juice of the nerves causes movement upon reaching the heart—the necessary mechanical causative event being the resulting explosive fermentation and inflation. The motions of muscles removed from the body cannot be due to causes different from those of motions of muscles in the living animal.

The Heart as Muscle Tissue, According to Borelli

Galen concluded, it will be recalled, that the heart was not like other muscles of the body because he found it to contain transverse fibers. He also noted that, when cooked, it tasted different from the other muscles. Regardless of its nature, however, nothing could be done with it experimentally, for there were no practical methods of studying any kind of muscle. Borelli (1608–79) reawakened interest in the heart's structure in his book *On the Motions of Animals* (1679), which presented a lucid statement of what could be learned about the heart as tissue without the aid of any special or novel tools. He brought a new outlook to physiology, and one that proved most fruitful. The discovery of current electricity a century or so later caused a veritable surge of investigative activity centering on muscle function.

Borelli begins by pointing out that the heart resembles other muscles in the body in its mode of action but differs from other muscles in that it is not subject to the will. Although many assert that cardiac motion is induced by "spiritual juices" from the nerves, yet the evidence is clear that the heartbeat continues after the nerves are severed. The heartbeat is like fire, or like the force of gravity inducing fall or flow. He compares it to the movement of the wind in the trees, ripples on the surface of water, the "tremblings of weights hanging on threads, and the quivering of green twigs." Best of all, he seems to favor comparing it to a clock, or to the swing of a pendulum.

What causes and controls this rhythmic motion? It is common knowledge that a porous sponge holds water that flows out only in drops, simulating regular spurts. The braking action of the sponge is due to the narrowness of the channels and to some adhesive force in the liquid particles; the flow can only be speeded by compression of the sponge. The heart continues beating after the severance of the nerves from the brain because its own nerves retain considerable quantities of the spirituous fluid. Borelli honors the same model of nerve function as the Doctors Lower and Mayow and manages quite well with it.

Why do other muscles, also provided with nerves, fail to show pulsations? To activate body muscles, the will must squeeze out spirits from the nerves. In the heart the flow is steady and rhythmic. Does the heart perhaps move "not by simple natural means but by those same animal faculties by which all muscles move?" The distinction is indeed subtle, although apparently real to the physiologists of the time. The explanation offered is equally misty. The pulsations of the heart stem from the emotions of grief and joy lodged in a given region of the brain, where certain nerves originate. The mind is concerned with good and evil and must therefore motivate those muscles "that anticipate the greatest good or threaten with the worst evil." The heart should not be affected by the mind but is. Since "it seems unbelievable that if the heart is moved only by one cause, it could be moved by others," it follows that "the customary movements of the heart are made not by mechanical instruments, or automatically, but by the living powers of sense and desire, which bring about strong pulsations in joy and curtail pulsations in fear."

Borelli performed no new experiments and presented no new ideas. However, he did call attention to the heart as a muscle in the first work completely dedicated to the study of muscles. In his book he declared that "seeing that muscles are the principal organs of animal motion, we must first examine their structure, parts, and visible action." He investigated individual muscles and then more complicated organs, until he came to analyze the overall problem of animal motion. His emphasis was on human movement, but he also discussed the locomotion of other mammals, the flight of birds, the swimming of fishes, and even the movements of insects and lower animals. His was primarily the approach of a mechanician, so that major attention was devoted to the mechanical aspects of such muscular exercises as walking, swimming, skating, jumping, running, and flying. Like one or two other writers of his day, he also proposed designs for submarines and for a diver's dress.

Borelli also dealt with the physiology of muscles. In this area he was obliged to be mostly speculative. He rejected the idea that contraction was caused by diminution of the muscle's mass and introduced the concept of the nerve impulse, expressed in the terms encountered in the text. The nervous spirits mix with the blood to produce fermentation in the muscle, which leads to its contraction. Thus, in spite of his preoccupation with mechanical principles, he introduced a chemico-physiological view of nervous conduction as well as muscular contraction. His ideas inspired researchers in the field of muscle action to think in terms of chemical events behind mechanical activity and to create and utilize new techniques and instruments.

19.
The Intricacy of Scientific Advance

This series of excerpts reviews the evolution of a relatively simple, fundamental physiological idea and the inception of a second, more complex one. Fragmentary as the texts are, they adequately illustrate one way in which science progresses and also afford a look at the gifted men who contribute to its advance. Each scientific venture is different in its strategy, obstacles, and victories, just as each scientist is different in his personality and approach to a problem. Nevertheless, some suggestive conclusions of general interest can be gleaned from the features of a single scientific process.

The concept of the blood's circulation took almost 2000 years to mature. That was the span of time from Herophilus' discovery of the distinction between veins and arteries and the isochronism of arterial pulsation and the heartbeat, through Erasistratus' detection of the valves in the heart and their connection with the flow of blood, to Leeuwenhoek's establishment of capillary anastomoses. The rather fanciful excuses offered by contemporary historians of science for the excessive length of this period of investigation are not surprising. We have seen, however, that the tyrranical domination of "the Galenic

tradition" was a fiction and that the Church's presumed prohibition of human dissection was not sufficient reason for the
slow growth of anatomical learning. Nor can it be maintained that the ancients did not know the meaning of data,
experimentation, or evidence. The works of Galen, Aristotle,
and Theophrastus in biology, and of Archimedes, Vitruvius,
and Seneca in the physical sciences, as well as those of the
early mathematicians, testify to the inaccuracy of this assertion. We must therefore seek elsewhere the causes of the
delay in making what seems superficially a straightforward
observation and deduction.

It is generally good policy to grant that if the conscious
intellectual efforts of a culture are hindered in arriving at a
certain technical, social, or moral truth, then the knowledge
in question is hard to come by. Although some incidental,
artificial forces may oppose the particular search, they must
be carefully evaluated before being deemed impediments.
The intrinsic difficulty must be admitted above all. The
records clearly show the laboriousness of each step in the
development of the idea of the circulation. Painstaking
accuracy in both perception and interpretation was impera-
tive. Despite repeated dissections and inspections of the veins,
the valves adhering to their walls were persistently overlooked, until a man of unique talent noticed them. Unfortunately, the explanation of such hitherto unrecognized
structures can lead into false or frustrating channels. It was
remarkable enough for Fabricius to demonstrate the valves
in the veins; it was still another matter for him to postulate a
function for them that would follow a consistent, productive,
and verifiable line of thought.

To account for omissions and misconceptions, we must
conclude that existing notions have the power of occasionally
obscuring new facts or of incorrectly molding them to the
reigning belief pattern. Hypotheses that have served well in
the past and may still be useful are not easily abandoned.
Given the concept of venous blood as a carrier of nutriment
and arterial blood as a carrier of pneuma, any idea of unity of
flow was likely to be rejected, should it have flashed into

someone's mind, and denied, should it have been openly proclaimed. Generations of anatomists failed to identify the venous valves lying in plain view, and Fabricius described them in terms of the only reference frame he had, the dominant belief-web. An occurrence that is contrary to the prevailing belief-web is normally regarded with dismay. It is as risky as a mutation, and just as essential to evolution.

Although the creative mind is forever restless and challenging, it is at the same time highly skilled at compromising and rationalizing. It can live at peace with a number of theories varying in validity and internal cohesion without discerning any of the inconsistencies and outright contradictions readily perceived by lesser minds of succeeding generations. It may seem pathetic that Fabricius naively missed the point of his own discovery, but it is even more pathetic that contemporary critics attribute his failure to an a priori fallacy or to his not having learned in his youth the difference between induction and deduction. Since his kind of "error" is noted in practically every one of the sources cited here, we must conclude that scientific reasoning is characterized by a tendency to fit new information into a familiar scheme. The only possible reply to Fabricius' own query as to why others had not reported the valves that were so strikingly apparent to him is that pertinent observations may be clouded, and even glaring gaps and discrepancies glossed over, when a prevailing belief-web explains most features satisfactorily. The more applicable the belief-web, the greater the dangers of oversight and of rationalization of inconsistencies.

A theory that is easily changed is like an institution, a language, or a government that is easily changed. Rapidly modifying the marriage laws causes confusion, and freely shifting the rules of a language produces the mess of Babel. Similarly, changing a scientific theory with every whim of an ambitious, unruly, and imaginative researcher can only destroy the science, not glorify it. On the other hand, testing each new idea even by sheer resistance, or pitting it against the will to maintain the status quo, strengthens the science. It should be remembered that the challenge to an established belief-web stems as a rule from notions arising from one angle of vision, or from one set of data. Since a belief-web is necessarily comprehensive, most scholars think of other areas in which it functions usefully and which the innovator may minimize. Thus Harvey never paused to explain how veins could carry nutriment if they merely brought blood back to the heart, or why he was so sure that the two vascular systems anastomosed invisibly, not for serving each other, but to unite the blood streams. Nevertheless, new theories, detrimental to the existing patterns, are born and grow. The men with whom they originate are honored by posterity because their contributions are rare and valuable. Their very novelty poses new questions, stimulates new activity, and invariably leads to new information. This enriches the scope and content of the science, attracts additional workers, and promotes further growth.

Any new theory that gains acceptance in the scientific community is a wonderful achievement, for it becomes a scaffolding for a new thought structure, even when it is fashioned from or colored by the ruling theory. Without such a framework there is only puttering and the accumulation of random data or concentration upon the worthless, the irrelevant, and the petty—in other words, either chaos or stagnation. A new theory redirects the gaze, initially at least stimulating the viewer with fresh sights and perspectives. Of course, a believer in evolution sees a newly discovered species in a different light from a believer in the permanency of species and special creation, just as a believer in phlogiston saw the reduction of mercuric oxide to mercury in a different light from a follower of the scheme proposed by Lavoisier.

New theories do not necessarily arise because of a crisis in the old belief-web, as some authorities claim. The fact is that they often read a crisis into a situation by hindsight. They assume that a new idea must appear when it does because of a need for it. They then select historical items to justify their reasoning. Undoubtedly there are occasions when the best minds are aware of the shortcomings of the current belief-web, but they do not always augur new theories. Conversely, new concepts about nature or society may emerge at any time from men like Aristarchus, Copernicus, Darwin, or Freud. Greek astronomy neither demanded nor expected Aristarchus, and it ignored him when he did appear. Copernicus' *On the Revolutions of the Celestial Spheres* was no more clamored for by the astronomers of his day than was Darwin's *Origin of Species* by the nineteenth-century biologists. The telescope would have enriched the science of the heavens and resulted in a new theory even without Copernicus; similarly, the work of Gregor Mendel and the discovery of the chromosomes would have led ultimately to the theory of evolution. The old belief-web concerning the origin and functions of the blood was in full force in 1628, when Harvey's classic was published, and by and large remained unchanged for decades thereafter. Yet Harvey's idea was inevitable, even though it could well have arisen later, in the trail of the great microscopists. However, history is opportunistic to a considerable degree, often introducing a genius long before the evidence for his vision is at hand. Moreover, there are always false prophets about, rebels eager to smash icons, doubters searching dogmas to attack, inquisitors satisfied only with harsh criticism. Those who make genuine contributions are tested and weighed with their offerings, and frequently judgment is rendered only after many years.

We should not assume that all progress results from the substitution of one belief-web for another. New belief-webs may or may not be awaited by the scientific family, may or may not be immediately productive, may or may not be destined to enjoy long reigns. Scientific advancement is complex and continuous. Whereas most workers apply or extend the tenets of the existing doctrine, verifying a circumstance here and there or exploring a new fact, ever so often a gifted human mind, normally functioning within the vise of its culture, strikes out to discover a new formula. If that formula is like the phlogiston or vortex theory, its life will be useful but brief. If it is like Harvey's idea of the circulation of the blood, or the heliocentric model of Copernicus, it will never be replaced. Subsequent learning may embellish it with the most elaborate ornamentation, but history will honor and cherish it, while other findings, equally hard-sought and even more enthusiastically hailed, may be completely discarded or relegated to some inconspicuous position.

As revolutionary as a new idea may seem, it is part and parcel of an earlier belief-web. No discovery is an item entirely apart; on the contrary, the old and the new are intimately linked. Thus Harvey's idea of the blood's circulation and Boyle's suspicions about hidden qualities in the air issued from a background of the old belief-web that generated and nurtured them and that seems so ridiculous today. What is significant is that the break with the past was not as complete as is often implied.

The contributors to scientific evolution are many and diverse. There are those who expand the influence of the controlling belief-web. There are those like Servetus and Columbus, who suggest concepts that may or may not be applied to a grander structure. There are those like Fabricius, who stumble upon the facts that inspire other minds to great achievements. And finally there are those like Harvey, who come forward with entirely new schemes, which, although they may contain many old elements, present them in wholly novel arrangements. There are equally brilliant and adventurous men whose innovations are eventually proven unworthy; such pioneers may be justly forgotten but often are unjustly maligned.

A new theory such as Harvey's can open up fascinating new vistas. His postulation of the circulation of the blood led to injections, transfusions, and the search for capillary anastomoses. It also probably affected the search for the mechanism of respiration, which opened still wider vistas.

Thus, however small the field covered by this account of the evolution of one biological idea and the partial development of another, the record furnishes an adequate and promising laboratory for a study of the nature of scientific thought and scientific progress. Critical examination of the facts of history, which constitute the data, reveals that the establishment of each concept was a far more complicated process than the stereotyped phraseology nowadays applied to the logic of science would indicate.

Index

Acosta, Josephus, 253
adaptation, 47
Against the Thesis of Harvey, 173
air, 42, 43, 48, 54, 64, 65, 81, 91, 110–11, 134, 184, 257; from bellows, 210; to brain, 69; to heart, 55, 69, 72, 104, 114; in insects, 195; in lungs, 177–79, 229–31; qualities of, 241–47; retention of, 114; salts in, 242–43, 248. *See also* respiration; spirit
air pressure, 226
air volume, 226
Albius, Andreas, 75
alcohol, 43
aliment, 54, 170
analogy, reasoning by, 195; role in innovation of, 53
anastomosis, 34, 38, 39, 40, 50, 51–52, 181–83, 184
anatomist, 47–48, 73, 77, 78, 95, 171, 269
anatomy, 45, 59, 74–77, 84, 100, 115, 175. *See also* dissection; vivisection
ancients, 2, 43, 73, 101, 268
animals, in closed chamber, 240; experiments on, 136–43, 198–202, 207–09, 223–24, 236, 250–52, 254–55, 259–62; movement of, 259–62, 264
animal spirit. *See* spirit, animal
antibodies, 205
aorta, 8, 13, 97, 98, 109, 149, 217
Apologetic Discourse in Favor of Astrology, An, 90
Apologia Against Leonhard Fuchs, An, 90
Archimedes, 2, 268
Aristarchus, 271
Aristotle, 2, 3, 5–11, 18, 44, 63, 77, 93, 96, 100, 102, 103–04, 108, 109–10, 111, 114, 115, 116, 117, 139–40, 148, 171, 268; errors of, 18
arteria venosa. *See* pulmonary vein

arteries, 29, 34, 71, 72, 80–81, 98, 113, 121, 155–56; blood in, 21–24, 131–32, 156–57, 187–89; in the brain, 87; distention of, 132; function of, 37–40, 130–31, 216–17; pulsation of, 14–15, 106, 108, 138–40; structure of, 13, 16, 43–44; tube in, 45. *See also* vascular system; vessels
Asclepion, 41
Aselli, Caspero, 174
astronomy, 2, 74, 115, 193, 271
atrium, 44
auricles, 18, 32–33, 44, 72; movement in, 140–43
authoritarianism, 2
Avicenna, 62, 90

Bartholin, Thomas, 174
belief-web, 48, 50, 81, 116, 170, 175, 226, 258, 269, 270
Bernard, Claude, 56
Bible, 172, 175
biology, 47, 170, 227
bladder stones, 77
blasphemy. *See* heresy
blood, in arteries, 21–24, 131–32, 156–57, 187–89; bilious, 127; color of, 42, 174, 220–23, 227; distribution of, 108, 113, 144; in embryo, 146–49; flow of, 27, 28–35, 50–52, 72, 81–82, 108–09, 112–13, 121–22, 123, 146, 150–53, 159–60, 163–65, 180–83, 195, 219–20, 264; general characteristics of, 8–9; melancholic, 127; motion of, 154–62; natural, 101, 102; pure, 85; purging of, 50; quantity, 154, 156–57; spirituous, 102; thick, 42, 64; thin, 60, 61, 101; vital, 101; warming of, 50, 112–14, 155, 163–64, 214
blood cells, 194
blood clots, 194, 219

blood groups, 205
blood transfusion, 197–203, 204–06, 223–25, 226
bond, covalent, 47
bones, 74, 80. *See also* ribs
Borelli, G. A., 184, 259–65
Boyle, Robert, 204, 210, 226, 239, 241–58, 272
brain, 10, 42, 69, 72, 87–89, 260, 263; function of, 215–16; purpose of, 114
breath, 42, 91
breathing. *See* respiration
Brock, A. J., 36
bronchi, 54, 60
Brozowski, H., 103
Bruno, Giordano, 73
burial, 78
Burke and Hale, 79

cadavers, 10, 74, 78–80
Caesalpinus, Andreas, 103–17
Calvin, John, 91
candle in closed chamber, 240
capillaries, 164–65, 185, 194, 195, 226. *See also* vascular system; vessels
Carpi, Berengario da, 76
Castiglioni, Arturo, 55
cell, 210. *See also* blood cells; sperm cells
Celsus, 2, 75
chemistry, organic, 47
Chirurgie, 100
Church, the, 74, 268
chyle, 164, 165, 170, 174, 204
chyme, 170
circulation, in eels, 191–92; in an embryo, 147; in frogs, 187–91; pulmonary, 83–84, 101–02, 116, 150–53; summary of, 267–73
cochlea, 48
coction, 48
Collected Works of Galen, 73
Columbus, Realdus, 93–102, 272
Commodus, 41
conduction by nerve, 265
contraction, 44, 45, 51, 264
convulsions, 210
Copernicus, 2, 271
corpuscles, aerial, 242–43, 246–47
correction factors, 51
criminals, for dissection, 75, 79; for injection, 204

Crocus Metallorum, 204
crystal structures, 194
culture, Greek, 1, 3; Hebrew, 1; primitive, 3

Dalton, J., 56
Darwin, Charles, 3, 56, 271
dead, disposal of, 78
debates, 41, 75
deduction, 56, 269
De Medicina, 75
demonstrations, 171, 175, 185. *See also* dissection
Denys, M., 198–203
Descartes, René, 173
DeWitt, N. J., 177
diaphragm, 233–34, 239
diastole. *See* pulsation
digestion, 48–49, 90
Diogenes, 6
Dionis, 175
Discours, 173
discoveries, 170, 184; role of, 126–27; voyages of, 227
dissection, 10, 15, 22–24, 41–42, 47, 59, 62, 74–75, 79–80, 131; errors in, 22–23; social restrictions on, 78–79. *See also* anatomy; vivisection
dogmatism, 55
Drebell, Cornelius, 254

embryology, 126, 146–49, 172, 173, 255–56; of chick, 175, 184
emotions, 264
Ent, Sir George, 173
epilepsy, 88
Erasistratus, 14, 24, 42, 43, 44, 46, 52, 75, 144–45, 267
"Erasistratus, Galen, and the 'Pneuma,'" 42, 43
Estienne, Charles, 77
Euclid, 2
evolution, 3, 269, 271
experiments, physico-mechanical, 250–56. *See also* animals, experiments on

Fabricius, Hieronymous, 3, 100, 118–27, 268–69, 272
Fallopius, 75, 77, 100, 171
fetal membranes, 126. *See also* embryology

Franklin, K. J., 119
Fuchs, Leonhard, 90
fuliginous particles, 53, 106
Fulton, John F., 77

Galen, 2, 3, 13–57, 63–65, 73, 74–75, 76, 77, 79, 80, 86, 90, 92, 95, 97, 98–99, 100, 102, 103, 104, 105–06, 110–11, 116, 117, 131, 144–45, 150, 151–52, 171, 194, 240, 263, 267, 268; errors of, 77
Galen of Pergamon, 47
Galileo, 2, 74, 126, 171, 193
gall bladder, 49
galls, 184
Garrison, Fielding H., 55
gaseous exchange, 227
Gassendi, Abbé Pierre, 173
Gayen, M., 201–03
germination of seeds, 194
gland, lymph, 184; pineal, 98
Graubard, M., 25, 259
Great Ideas in the History of Surgery, 101
Gunther, R. T., 213
Gurye de Montpoly, Gasper de, 197–201, 205

Haddad, S. I., 59
haemorrhage, 45
Hall, A. R., 56
Handbook in Anatomy, A, 174
Harvey, William, 2, 3, 4, 56, 100, 129–76, 194, 226, 272
heart, 7–8, 60; cavities of. *See* ventricles; in embryo, 146–49, 167; fat surrounding, 93–94; function of, 39, 61–62, 104–05, 143–45; as furnace, 102; Galen's concept of, 53–54; pulsation of, 17–18, 46, 49, 51, 105–09, 129, 135–38, 142, 157–58, 161, 213–14, 215, 217–19, 238, 259–62, 263; and respiration, 25–26; soot, 46; structure of, 7, 16–17, 19, 67–68, 93–99, 167–68, 237; as tissue, 263; in various species, 165–67; vessels of, 96–97
heartbeat, 44, 45, 46, 49, 51, 227, 259–65, 267
heat, 25–26, 53, 69, 81, 88–89, 104, 112–14, 226; innate, 46; natural, 53
herbs, 226

heresy, 90, 101
Hero, 2
Herophilus, 10, 44, 75, 267
Hippocrates, 2, 10, 73, 90, 100, 255
histology, 184
History of Animals, 3
History of Botany, 116
Hooke, Robert, 207–11, 226, 239
Hoole, S., 187

iatrochemists, 258
Ibn Nafis, 59–65
induction, 56, 269

James I., 172
Jenner, Edward, 3

Kepler, J., 193
Khairallah, A. A., 59

Laguna, Andreas de, 76
larynx, 54, 126
Laurentius, Andreas, 136
Lavoisier, 270
Leake, C. D., 129
Leeuwenhoek, Antony van, 187–95, 267
lens, 44, 193
ligatures, 45, 158–60
Lind, L. R., 67, 74
liver, 48, 49, 64, 101, 150–51, 165, 170
Lower, Richard, 204, 213–28, 239, 264
lumen, 216–17
lungs, 19, 26, 27–29, 42, 102, 116, 184, 210, 240; blood in, 221–22; in embryo, 146–49; experiments on, 207–09; function of, 104–05, 112–14, 150–53, 229–31, 235–36; Galen's concept of, 54; nourishment of, 114, 133; structure of, 60–61, 68–69, 177–79, 181–83
lymphatics, 174

Malpighi, Marcello, 177–85, 239
Manual of Anatomy, 175
Marcus Aurelius, 41
Marinus, 44
Massa, Nicolaus, 77
Mayow, John, 226, 229–40, 264
Medici, Cosimo de, 75
medicine, 90, 115, 170, 171, 226, 239
Mendel, Gregor, 51, 271

meninx(ges), 87–88
Mersenne, 173
mesentery, peritoneal, 174
Method of Treatment, 43
microscope, 185, 193–94, 210
model, Galen's, 55, 57, 170; heliocentric, 271
Mondeville, Henri de, 100
Mondino, 76
Montagu, M. F. Ashley, 77
muscles, 44, 176, 240, 263, 264: of heart, 44, 263. *See also* heartbeat; movement of, 259–62; voluntary, 44
mutation, 269
movements, spontaneous and voluntary, 55

natural selection, 47, 48
nature, opportunistic aspects of, 53; purpose in, 46, 47, 48
nerve impulse, 227, 265
nerves, 17, 44, 87–88, 263
Newton, Isaac, 210, 239
nightmares, 234, 239
nitro-aerial particles, 236–38, 240
nourishment, 26–29, 34–35, 39, 52–53, 72, 114, 127, 133, 151, 194
nutriment, 50, 113, 268

Observationes Anatomicae, 77
O'Malley, C. D., 83
On Generation in Animals, 173
On Plants, 115
On the Development of the Eggs of Birds, 126
On the Fabric of the Human Body, 75
On the Formed Foetus, 126
On the Heart, 226
On the Opinions of Hippocrates and Plato, 42
On the Revolutions of the Celestial Spheres, 271
opium, 204
organs, 50, 74, 100, 127, 176, 194, 210, 264
Origin of Species, 271
oxygen, 227, 240, 243–44

palpitation, 218
Pappus, 2
Paracelsus, 73, 254, 258
paralysis, 44
parasites, 194

Parisano, Emilio, 173
passion, 43, 101. *See also* emotion
Pasteur, Louis, 3
Patin, Guy, 173
Payen, Sieur, 174
Pecquet, Jean, 174
Petty, Sir William, 210
pharynx, 54
Philosophical Transactions, 204
phlebotomy, 226
phlogiston, 270
Physicus, Partius Neopolitanus, 93
physiology, 263, 264
placenta, 126
plasma, 195
pleurisy, 52
plexuses, 86–87
Pliny, 2
pneuma, 14, 15, 27, 35, 42–43, 46, 49, 54, 257, 268
pneumonia, 52
pores, 34–35, 52, 64, 101, 108, 134–35, 240
pressure, atmospheric, 239
Primerose, James, 173
Ptolemy, 2
pulmonary artery, 15, 26–27, 28, 43, 50, 51, 54, 60, 61, 86, 94, 96, 97, 102, 113, 133, 151–52, 168–69
pulmonary vein, 14–15, 26–27, 28, 43–44, 50, 54, 55, 86, 94–95, 96, 97, 102, 105–06, 113, 133, 134, 151–52, 168–69
pulsation, 14–15, 17–18, 20–21, 46, 51, 105–09, 129–31, 135–43, 157–58, 161, 213–14, 215, 217–19, 238, 259–62, 264, 267. *See also* heart, pulsation of
pulse, 42, 43, 45–46, 69, 132, 165, 194

Rath, G., 77
Rationalists, 75
rationalizations, 48, 49, 51, 258, 269
refrigeration, 53, 79
regimen, 226
Reid, Alexander, 175
religion, and science, 2, 78, 91, 267–68
reproduction, 172
respiration, 25–26, 27–29, 53, 69, 72, 81, 85, 89, 103–05, 109–12, 226, 229–40, 250–56, 257. *See also* air
rete mirabile, 42

ribs, 232–33, 239
Riolan, Jean, 46, 173
Royal Society of London, 194, 204, 210, 239

Sachs, J. von, 116
Saint Augustine, 2
sanity, 228
Sarton, George, 47, 55
Sceptical Chymist, The, 257
scheme, as model, 65, 81, 127, 171, 194, 227, 263, 269
science, advance of, 1–4, 267–73; and religion. *See* religion
Science, Medicine and History, 77
scientific method, 210
Second Letter of William Harvey, 46, 174
sella turcica, 48
Seneca, 268
sensations, 42
sense organs, 126
septum, interventricular, 52, 63, 64
Servetus, Michael, 65, 83–92, 101, 102, 272
Short History of Anatomy and Physiology, A, 55, 75, 80
Singer, Charles, 13, 47, 55, 75–76
skull, 48
sleep, 239
sounds, production of, 126
Spencer, W. G., 75
spirit, 43, 64, 101, 102, 108, 174, 259; animal, 53, 60, 61, 62, 101, 127, 227, 237; divine, 84–85; vital, 72, 84, 85, 86, 106, 127, 134, 257
spiritual juices, 263
spleen, 49
Starry Messenger, The, 193
superstition, 11, 45, 73
surgery, 77, 226, 239
Syennesis, 6
Syrups Carefully Refined According to the Judgment of Galen, Complete Account of, 90
systole. *See* pulsation

teleology, 47, 48, 51, 56, 115
telescope, 193, 271
Theophrastus, 2, 268
Thompson, D. W., 5, 10
thorax, 27–28, 54, 55, 68, 69, 233

Thorndike, Lynn, 90
tissue, 10, 54, 194, 210
trachea, 54, 103, 106, 114

Underwood, E. A., 77
uterus, 126

valves, 29–31, 33–34, 51, 102, 109, 119–25, 127, 133, 151–52, 160–62, 173, 267, 268–69; mitral, 113, 134
vascular system, 10, 80. *See also* arteries; capillaries; veins; vessels
veins, 5–7, 28–29, 34, 43–44, 80–81, 113, 124, 155–56; function of, 119–25; structure of, 16, 43–44; valves in, 160–62. *See also* vascular system; vessels
Veith, I., 101
vena arteriosa. *See* pulmonary artery
vena cava, 11, 67, 70, 72, 86, 94, 96, 102, 109, 113, 120, 122, 146, 147–48, 152, 153, 217
venesection, 45
venous artery, 19
venous blood, 49
ventricles, 86, 94, 112–13, 166–67; blood quantity in, 156; in the brain, 88; movement in, 140, 141; structure of, 67–68, 133
Vesalius, Andreas, 2, 3, 67–82, 98, 100; errors of, 77
Vesalius Four Centuries Later, 77
Vesling, Johann, 174
vessels, 10, 112–13, 155–56, 190–91; in the brain, 87–88; of the heart, 96–97; lacteal, 174. *See also* arteries; capillaries; vascular system; veins
viscera, 48, 53, 75, 233
Vitruvius, 2, 268
vivisection, 19–21, 45
voice, 46, 53

Whether Blood Is Contained in the Arteries in Nature, 43, 45
Wilson, L. G., 42
witchcraft, 172, 175
Wren, Christopher, 204, 210, 239

Young, James, 180

Zimmerman, L. M., 101

343504E
6R4